Nelson Advanced Modular Science

Matter and Waves

MARK ELLSE • CHRIS HONEYWILL

Nelson

Thomas Nelson UK
Nelson House
Mayfield Road
Walton-on-Thames
Surrey
KT12 5PL   United Kingdom

First published by Thomas Nelson and Sons Ltd 1998

I(T)P Thomas Nelson is an International Thomson Publishing Company
I(T)P is used under licence

ISBN 0-17-448261-2
NPN 9 8 7 6 5 4 3

Printed in China
Picture Research by Image Select International Limited
Publishing team:
Staff editorial: Simon Bell
Freelance editorial: Geoff Amor
Production: Alison Ealden/Suzanne Howarth
Design/Typesetting: Hardlines, Charlbury, Oxford

Contents

Preface

This book takes you through the second Module of the Edexcel London Examinations A-level and AS-level Physics syllabus. It is also suitable for the core content of other A-level schemes. We have divided the book into small chapters, each of which introduces only a few new ideas.

Within the chapters are suggestions for experiments. You may not do or see all the experiments, but you should think about them as you read the text and try to predict what the experiments would show. Most of the experiments are described in a way that you could use yourself as an answer to an examination question that required an experimental description.

Important terms are highlighted in **bold**. There is a list of these terms, under the heading 'Things you need to know', on pages 86–89 of this book.

On pages 75–80 you will find practice questions to try after studying each chapter. There is also a selection of past examination questions on pages 81–85.

The chapters are in a possible teaching order, but as far as possible we have tried to make them self-contained, so that you can use them in any order, or dip into them for revision.

This book is one of a series of four Module texts for Edexcel London Examinations A-level Physics. Alongside them is published a set of Experiment Sheets by Adrian Watt, which describe in greater detail how to carry out many of the experiments in the texts.

Mark Ellse is Director of Chase Academy, Cannock, Staffordshire, and a Principal Examiner for Edexcel London Examinations.

Chris Honeywill was Deputy Registrar and Head of Physics at The Sixth Form College, Farnborough, Hampshire, and is an Assistant Principal Examiner for Edexcel London Examinations.

Acknowledgements

The authors and publishers are grateful for the kind assistance of David Hartley, Mike Chapple and John Warren for their painstaking work in reading and commenting on the manuscripts, and John Harris for his work preparing many of the diagrams.

The authors and publishers are grateful to the following for permission to reproduce copyright photographs.

Philippe Plailly/Science Photo Library: Half-title page 1; Alan Thomas: Figures 1.6 to 1.9, page 3; Figure 3.2, page 7; Figure 14.5, page 35; Figure 15.3, page 37; Image Select/James Clift: Figure 2.3, page 4; Image Select/Chris Fairclough: Figure 2.5, page 5; Figure 6.1, page 12; Image Select: Figure 7.1, page 15; Andrew Syred/Science Photo Library: Figure 3.3, page 7; Manfred Kage/Science Photo Library: Figure 3.4, page 7; Erich Schrempp/Science Photo Library: Figure 7.4, page 16; John Mason/Science Photo Library: Figure 9.5, page 23 Simon Fraser/Science Photo Library: Half-title page 27; Hulton Getty: Figure 15.4, page 37; Peter Gould: Figures 25.4 and 25.5, page 57; Oliver Benn/Tony Stone Worldwide: Figure 26.6, page 60; Keith MacGregor/Tony Stone Worldwide: Half-title page 61; Department of Physics, Imperial College/Science Photo Library: Figure 29.6 (top, centre and bottom);

Materials and matter

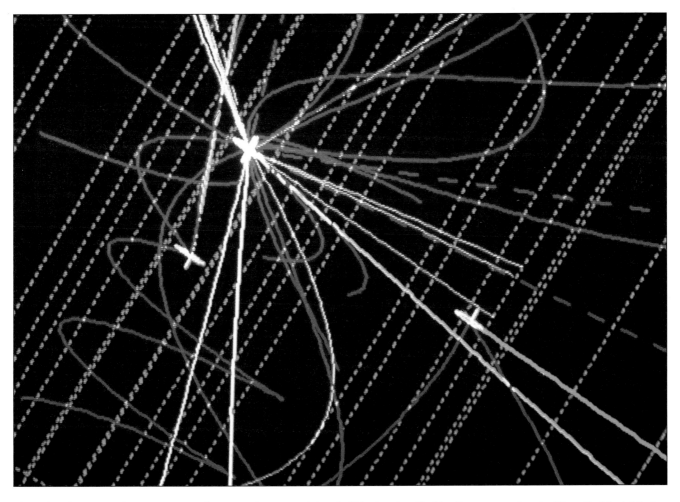

The paths of matter and antimatter (an electron and a positron) in a bubble chamber. The blue lines represent part of the cylindrical detector.

Making measurements precisely

Figure 1.1   The rule can measure to a resolution of 1 mm

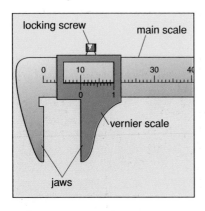

Figure 1.2   The zero on the vernier scale is at the same end of the scale as the zero on the main scale. It has ten divisions in a length of 9 mm, which means that only one of its marks coincides exactly with a mark on the main scale

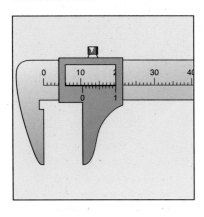

Resolution

The **resolution** of a measuring instrument is the smallest difference it can measure, usually the smallest scale division. The scale divisions on the metre rule shown in Figure 1.1 are 1 mm apart. The diameter of the 5p coin it is measuring is 18 mm to a resolution of 1 mm.

Accuracy

The **accuracy** of a measuring instrument is the difference between the reading it indicates and the true reading. No measuring instrument can be more accurate than its resolution; for instance, a metre rule cannot measure more accurately than to within 1 mm. But accuracy can be much worse than the resolution; for instance, a wooden metre rule may have shrunk and have an error of several millimetres in a metre.

Vernier scales

Vernier scales are used to divide a wide range of scales into smaller divisions and so provide better resolution. They are commonly used to divide a scale with millimetre divisions into tenths, and so provide a resolution of a tenth of a millimetre (0.1 mm). Vernier scales are common on scales for measuring extensions of stretched wires.

Figures 1.2 to 1.5 show how to use **vernier callipers** to measure the diameter of a 5p coin.

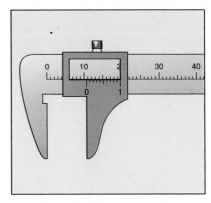

Figure 1.3   Close the callipers and check that the two zeros coincide. Then open the callipers 10 mm and check that the only mark on the vernier that coincides exactly with the main scale is the zero on the vernier scale. Then ease the callipers half a millimetre further open to 10.5 mm. The zero on the vernier scale is half-way between the 10 mm and 11 mm marks, and the fifth mark on the vernier scale coincides with the mark above it on the main scale

Figure 1.4   Here the callipers are open 10.7 mm the seventh division on the vernier scale coincides exactly with the main scale

Micrometer screw gauges

The **micrometer screw gauge** uses a screw thread to measure distances to a resolution of a hundredth of a millimetre (0.01 mm).

Figures 1.6 to 1.9 show you how to use the micrometer screw gauge to measure the diameter of a 5p coin.

Uncertainty

No reading of a physical quantity is exact. All readings have some **uncertainty** the range around the measured reading within which the true reading lies. If you read a measuring instrument to one scale division, the uncertainty is at least half a scale division. For instance, an accurate metre rule has an uncertainty of ± 0.5 mm, because a reading could be up to 0.5 mm above or below a scale division and still be quoted as being on that division.

Percentage uncertainty

An uncertainty of 0.5 mm is not important in measuring the height of a building, but would be significant in measuring the diameter of a pencil. You can measure the importance of an uncertainty by dividing the uncertainty by the reading and expressing the result as a percentage:

$$\text{percentage uncertainty} = \frac{\text{uncertainty}}{\text{average value}} \times 100\%$$

So if a table 750 mm long were measured with a metre rule, the uncertainty is ±0.5 mm, and

$$\text{percentage uncertainty} = \frac{\pm 0.5 \text{ mm}}{750 \text{ mm}} \times 100\% = \pm 0.07\%$$

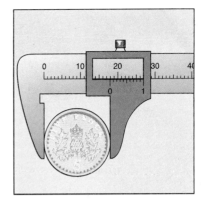

Figure 1.5   Place a 5p coin in the callipers. First take the reading on the main scale. It is between 17 mm and 18 mm. Then read the vernier scale to find the number of tenth-millimetre divisions–in this case nine tenths, 0.9 mm. So the diameter of the coin is 17.9 mm to a resolution of 0.1 mm

Figure 1.6   First close the micrometer and check that the scale on the rotating barrel reads zero. Then unscrew the barrel two complete turns. You will find that the gap is 1 mm

Figure 1.7 Reduce the gap to 0.5 mm by screwing the barrel back one turn. The first 0.5 mm mark is just visible and the scale on the barrel reads zero. The jaws move 0.5 mm for each turn of the screw and the rotating scale divides this 0.5 mm into 50 divisions, each of 0.01 mm

Figure 1.8 Rotate the screw half a turn outwards. The gap is 0.5 mm (shown on the fixed scale) plus 0.25 mm (shown on the barrel), which is a total of 0.75 mm

Figure 1.9   Place a 5p coin in the micrometer. Add the fixed scale reading (17.5 mm) to the barrel reading (0.39 mm) to find the diameter of the coin (17.89 mm) to a resolution of 0.01 mm

Measuring density

- Measure the masses in kilograms of a range of solid objects. Then measure their volumes. Use a micrometer or vernier callipers to measure their dimensions if they are regular, or use the method shown in Figure 2.1 if the solids are irregular. Calculate their volumes in metres cubed. Divide the masses by the volumes to find the densities.
- Measure the mass of a measuring cylinder; then add a known volume of liquid to it and measure the total mass. Find the mass of liquid added. Divide the mass of the liquid by its volume to find the density of the liquid.
- Find the density of a cube of ice. Then watch it melt into a measuring cylinder and measure its density again. Carry out a similar experiment with a cube of wax. How much, in general, do substances change in volume when they change from solids to liquids?
- Measure the mass and volume of a small cube of solid carbon dioxide. Drop it into a plastic bag and seal the bag (Figure 2.2). Estimate the volume when all the carbon dioxide has become gas. Calculate the density of solid carbon dioxide and that of gaseous carbon dioxide.

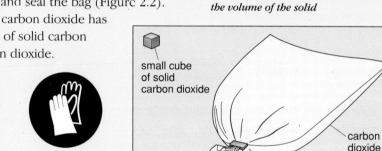

Figure 2.1 *Immerse an irregular solid in a measuring cylinder of liquid. The increase in scale indicated by the changing liquid level is equal to the volume of the solid*

HAZARD
dry ice burns

EYE PROTECTION
MUST BE WORN

HAND
PROTECTION
MUST BE WORN

Figure 2.2 *Carbon dioxide cube and inflated bag*

Density

The **density** of an object is its mass divided by its volume:

$$\text{density} = \frac{\text{mass}}{\text{volume}} \quad \text{or} \quad \rho = \frac{m}{V}$$

(The symbol ρ is a Greek letter *rho*, pronounced as in 'row the boat'.)

Common, and convenient, units for density are grams per centimetre cubed and kilograms per litre. But the SI unit of density is kilograms per metre cubed (kg m^{-3}), which is sometimes hard to think about unless you remind yourself of how big a metre cubed is.

The density of water is 1000 kg m^{-3}, and since 1000 kg is a tonne (t), you could express this as 1 t m^{-3}.

The range of densities

Table 2.1 shows the densities of a range of substances. As you can see, the densities of solids and liquids overlap, and there is no simple rule for which is denser. Solids change little in volume when they are melted, so for a given substance, the densities of the solid and liquid are similar. But there is a very large change in volume from liquid to gas, so the density of any gas is much less than the density of any solid or liquid.

How compressible?

- Try to compress a plastic syringe of air.
- Repeat with water.
- Then put a piece of dowel into a syringe and try to compress that.
- Compare the compressibilities with the densities.

Compressibilities

A fairly small force, which has no noticeable effect on a liquid or a solid, will cause a large fractional reduction in the volume of a gas. Chapter 3 shows how this, along with the fact that the densities of solids and liquids are much greater than those of gases, gives some idea of the microscopic differences between solids and liquids, on the one hand, and gases, on the other.

Solids and fluids

Solids are **rigid**; they keep their shape. You can use solid objects to transmit forces, along a series of levers, for instance.

Gases and liquids are **fluid**. They flow to fit the shape of their container.

Pressure

When you compress fluids, they exert forces perpendicular to the sides of the containers that constrain them. They exert equal forces on equal areas. So if the area is doubled, the force on it is doubled, but the force per unit area, the **pressure**, stays the same. The size of the pressure is calculated by dividing the (perpendicular) force by the area over which it acts:

pressure = force/area or $p = F/A$

The units of pressure are N m^{-2}, called the pascal (Pa).

Pneumatic and hydraulic systems

- Connect together plastic syringes of equal size. Feel what happens when you push one syringe. This is a simple example of a pneumatic system (Figure 2.3).
- Repeat the experiment with the syringes filled with water. This is a simple example of a hydraulic system (Figure 2.4).
- Predict what will happen if the syringes are of different cross-sectional areas. Then try it.

Table 2.1 *Densities of some substances*

Substance	Density/kg m⁻³ at room temperature and pressure
platinum	21400
mercury	13600
iron	8000
aluminium	2700
glass	2500
water	1000
ice	917 (at −4°C)
ethanol	790
wood (oak)	c. 700
wood (balsa)	c. 200
carbon dioxide	1.9
air	1.3
methane	0.7
hydrogen	0.09

Figure 2.3 Pneumatic systems use air pressure

Figure 2.4 Hydraulic systems usually use oil as the liquid

3 | The structure of matter

Figure 3.1 Electron microscope image of the surface of aluminium

Matter is made up of particles

Figure 3.1 shows an electron microscope image of the surface of a metal. This gives strong evidence that the metal is made of a large number of identical particles fitted together in a regular way.

Close and distant

You know that solids and liquids are hard to compress. From this, you can deduce that the particles in solids and liquids are themselves hard to compress, and there is little space between them.

The density of a substance drops considerably when it becomes a gas, and gases themselves are easy to compress. From this, and other evidence, you can deduce that there are large spaces between the particles in a gas.

Fixed and free

Solids keep their shape and they can transmit forces. So there must be forces between the particles. Liquids take the shape of the container, but stay together as drops. Again, there must be forces between the particles, but the forces do not keep the particles in fixed positions.

Gases not only flow, but also spread out to fill the container they are in, however big it might be. This suggests that any attractive forces between the particles are very small.

Table 3.1 gives a summary of the structure and properties of the different states of matter, and some information about the motion of the particles, about which you can learn more in Module 3.

State	Molecular structure	Physical properties
Solid	close molecular packing	dense, incompressible
	fixed molecular positions	rigid, transmit forces
	vibrate about fixed positions	expand when heated
	strong bonds	hard to pull apart
	generally have long-range order can be amorphous, polycrystalline or crystalline	crystalline properties often externally observable
Liquid	close molecular packing	dense, incompressible (transmit pressures)
	randomly arranged and free to change position	take shape of container, fluid (not rigid), do not transmit forces
	bonds quite strong	quite hard to pull liquids apart – leads to surface tension
	no long-range order	amorphous structure means that no structural arrangement is discernible from outside
Gas	particles far apart	not dense, easily compressible
	moving about randomly	fill available space, cause pressure by hitting walls, transmit pressures but not forces
	no bonds	expand for ever
	no order at all	

Table 3.1 *Molecular structure and its consequences*

Crystals

If you have a number of identical particles and put them together, they tend to form patterns. The atoms in an element are identical. When a liquid solidifies, the particles usually arrange themselves in similar regular patterns. This means that the arrangement of atoms in most solids is not irregular – it is ordered. A **crystal** is a collection of atoms with a regular structure.

The layers of atoms in a solid metal element often have a hexagonal structure like the balls in Figure 3.2.

Figure 3.2 Stacking balls in a frame

Large and small crystals

If you solidify a liquid very slowly, the crystals that form are large, because there is time for the particles to arrange themselves in a very ordered way. Some solids, for instance ionic solids like common salt (Figure 3.3), can only solidify in a crystalline way.

If a liquid solidifies quickly, crystals form in many different places, all at the same time. When all has solidified, the solid is **polycrystalline**; it is made of many crystals aligned in different directions. Though it is possible to make large single metal crystals, the structure of most metals you come across is polycrystalline (Figure 3.4).

If you solidify a liquid very quickly indeed, there is no time for the atoms to arrange themselves regularly. This forms an **amorphous** solid (literally a solid *without shape*). Glass is amorphous; you have to cool it very slowly indeed to make crystals.

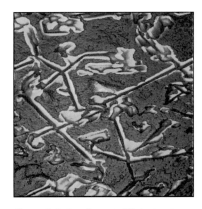

Figure 3.3 Salt crystals

Polymers

Carbon can join with other atoms to form long chain molecules called **polymers**. Some polymers, like rubber, starch and cellulose, occur naturally; people have made other polymers, like polyethene and nylon.

The molecules in a polymeric solid can be regularly arranged, in which case the polymer is crystalline; or the molecules may be randomly arranged, and the polymer is amorphous. If the arrangement is partly random and partly ordered, the polymer is semicrystalline.

Ordinary rubber, like that in a toy balloon, is made up of long chain molecules tangled together – it is amorphous. The molecules line up when you stretch it, so it becomes crystalline.

Figure 3.4 A polycrystalline structure

Investigating structure

- Break a piece of cast iron. Examine the crystals with a hand lens.
- Take a crystal of calcite. Try chopping it in different directions with a hammer and razor blade. What do you deduce about the structure?
- Pierce a piece of balloon rubber with a pin and try to 'stir' the pin around. Then stretch the rubber and repeat.
- Stretch the rubber at right angles to the original direction and stir again.

EYE PROTECTION
MUST BE WORN

4 | Tension and extension

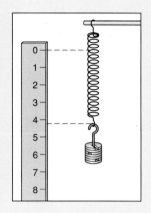
Proportionality

The first part of the tension–extension graph for a spring is a straight line. Robert Hooke produced a law about the behaviour of materials. When applied to springs, **Hooke's law** states that, up to a limit, the extension of a spring is proportional to the tension. Mathematically, tension ∝ extension, which can be written in symbols as

$$F \propto x \quad \text{or} \quad F = kx$$

where k is a constant called the **spring constant**.

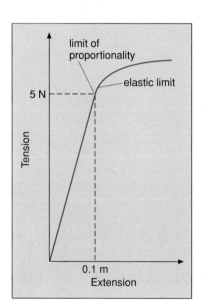

Figure 4.2 Graph for spring

If tension is measured in newtons (N) and extension in metres (m), then k has units of newtons per metre (N m^{-1}). You can think of the spring constant as a measure of the stiffness of the spring. A **stiff** spring has a larger spring constant than a flexible spring; the stiff spring needs a larger tension than the flexible spring for a given extension.

The spring whose graph is shown in Figure 4.2 has a spring constant of 50 N m^{-1}; it would need 50 N to extend it a metre (if you could extend it that far!).

Above a certain tension, the spring graph is no longer a straight line; the extension is no longer proportional to the tension. The point above which this happens is called the **limit of proportionality**, or sometimes the *Hooke's law limit*.

Elasticity

If you apply a small tension to a spring and then remove that tension, the spring returns to its original length. This is true up to a limit, called the **elastic limit**.

Below the elastic limit, the spring is **elastic**; extensions of the spring are not permanent. When you remove the tension, the extension returns to zero.

Beyond the elastic limit, the spring's behaviour is **plastic**; it deforms permanently. When you remove the tension, the extension does not return to zero. You cannot find the elastic limit by looking at a graph, only by experimenting to find the smallest tension that produces a permanent extension.

You can see from their definitions that the *elastic limit* and the *limit of proportionality* are quite different in meaning, but for a spring the two limits are very close together. As you can see from Figure 4.2, the elastic limit comes just after the limit of proportionality.

Measuring energy stored in a spring

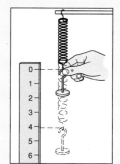

- Hold a 100 g mass hanger with the hook just above the bottom loop of the spring (Figure 4.3). Release the mass hanger and measure the maximum extension of the spring when the mass hanger reaches the bottom of its travel.
- Calculate the potential energy lost by the mass hanger falling. What is the kinetic energy of the mass and spring at the bottom of the fall? What energy is stored in the spring?
- Repeat, increasing the falling mass in 100 g steps.
- Plot a graph of energy stored in the spring against extension. What relationship do you observe?

 If your falling mass goes above a few hundred grammes, keep your feet and hands out of harm's way.

Figure 4.3 Dropping mass onto spring

Energy stored in a spring

If you stretch a spring elastically, the energy stored in the spring is equal to the work done stretching it. Figure 4.4 shows the proportional part of a tension–extension graph for a spring. The work done stretching it a small distance Δx (Δ is the Greek letter *delta*) with a force F is given by

$$\text{work done } = \text{ force } \times \text{ distance } = F\Delta x$$

This is the area of the shaded strip. As you learned in *Mechanics and Electricity*, the total work done in stretching from zero to extension x is equal to the total area between the graph and the extension axis.

Since the tension is proportional to the extension, the area under the graph, which is the energy stored, is triangular. The area is given by

$$\text{area } = \tfrac{1}{2} \times \text{ base } \times \text{ height } = \tfrac{1}{2} \times \text{ tension } \times \text{ extension}$$

So the energy stored in the spring is

$$W = \tfrac{1}{2}Fx$$

Since $F = kx$, we get

$$W = \tfrac{1}{2}(kx)x = \tfrac{1}{2}kx^2$$

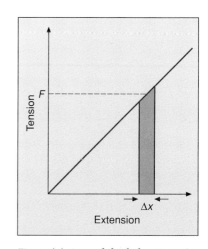

Figure 4.4 Area of shaded strip is $F\Delta x$

5 Stretching materials

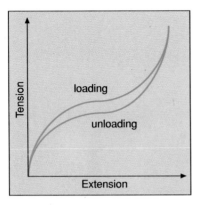

Figure 5.1 Tension–extension graph for a rubber band

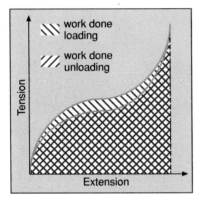

Figure 5.2 Loading and unloading

The behaviour of rubber

For rubber, extension is not proportional to tension. So a tension–extension graph is very far from a straight line. The shape of the graph in Figure 5.1 gives you some idea of what is happening inside the rubber as you stretch it.

You learned in Chapter 3 that rubber is made of tangled chain molecules. When you apply small tensions to the rubber, you start straightening out the chains. This is a relatively easy process; the rubber is not stiff, and it needs a comparatively small tension for a given extension.

As the extension of the rubber band increases, the chains become straighter and are then harder to stretch. The rubber is then stiffer; it needs a larger tension for a given extension.

When you remove the load from a rubber band, it returns more or less to its original length. But the unloading graph is below the loading graph, as shown in Figure 5.1.

You know that the work done stretching something is the area enclosed by the tension–extension graph and the extension axis. Similarly, the work done by the same specimen unloading is the area under the unloading tension–extension graph. For a spring, the loading and unloading graphs are identical, meaning that the work done *on* the spring loading it is equal to the work done *by* the spring unloading. For a rubber band, the area under the unloading graph is less than the area under the loading graph, meaning that the band does less work unloading than the work done on it when loading.

The energy difference is equal to the area between the loading and unloading graphs, as shown in Figure 5.2. This energy raises the temperature of the band and the surroundings.

Stretching copper

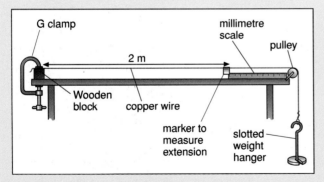

Figure 5.3 Stretching copper wire

- Take a long length of thin copper wire and fasten it to a long bench as shown in Figure 5.3.
- Measure the extension of the wire for a range of tensions.
- Unload and reload, measuring the tensions and extensions part-way through your experiment.
- Plot a graph of tension against extension.

EYE PROTECTION
MUST BE WORN

The behaviour of copper

The tension–extension graph for copper is a straight line where the extension is small, showing that extension is proportional to tension (Figure 5.4). The copper is elastic in this region – the extension returns to zero if the force (tension) is removed. In this region of the graph, forces applied to the copper slightly increase the distance between its atoms without changing the positions of the atoms. The forces stretch the atomic bonds without breaking them. This elastic behaviour does not absorb energy – the work done *on* the copper when you stretch it is equal to the work done *by* the copper when it is released.

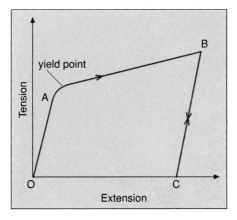

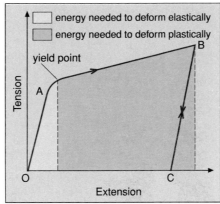

Figure 5.4 Tension–extension graph for copper

Figure 5.5 The energy needed to stretch a copper wire

If you stretch copper past the linear region, it deforms permanently. Some of the atoms slide over each other; this is called **plastic flow**. Plastic flow occurs after the **yield point**, the elastic limit for a wire. Forces that take the copper above the yield point break bonds between atoms in the copper and rearrange them. When you remove the force, the atoms are unable to return to their original positions. Plastic deformation absorbs energy. Some energy is used to break bonds; some is used to raise the temperature of the copper as the atoms slide over each other.

The energy needed to stretch a copper wire elastically is the relatively small area under the first part of the tension–extension graph (Figure 5.5). The energy used to stretch it plastically to breaking is much greater.

Pre-stretched copper

If you unload and reload a copper wire after it has undergone some plastic flow, the graph is a straight line (BC) parallel to the first loading line (line OA in Figure 5.4). If you were given a piece of pre-stretched copper wire to test, you would get a graph like that of Figure 5.6. You can see that Figure 5.6 is merely the final part of Figure 5.4.

Copper wire straight from the reel is **tough**. It can absorb large amounts of energy by plastic deformation, so it needs a lot of energy to break it. Pre-stretched copper wire is **brittle**. It cannot absorb energy by plastic deformation, so needs little energy to break it.

Mild steel, as used in car bodies, is tough, and can absorb much of the energy involved in a car crash, which means that less is available to damage the passengers.

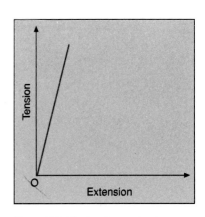

Figure 5.6 The tension–extension graph for pre-stretched copper

Stress, strain and the Young modulus

Figure 6.1 These steel cables break under a tension of 300 kN

Stress and strain

The strength of a wire depends on its cross-sectional area. Thicker wires are stronger than thinner wires of the same material.

For a given material, the tension needed to break the wire divided by the cross-sectional area is constant. The tension divided by cross-sectional area is called the **tensile stress**, symbol σ (the small Greek letter *sigma*):

$$\text{tensile stress} = \frac{\text{tension}}{\text{cross-sectional area}}$$

Stress has the same units as pressure, the newton per metre squared, or the pascal (Pa).

The stress needed to break a material is called the **breaking stress** or **ultimate tensile stress**. If you want to compare the strengths of different materials, you compare the breaking stresses, since these do not depend on the cross-sectional area of the sample that you are testing. A strong material like steel (Figure 6.1) has a high ultimate tensile stress; a weak material has a low ultimate tensile stress.

A steel wire, cross-sectional area 1.0 mm² breaks under a tension of 250 N. Then

$$\text{breaking stress} = F/A = 250 \text{ N}/(1.0 \times 10^{-6} \text{ m}^2) = 250 \text{ MPa}$$

The shape of a tension–extension graph depends on the dimensions of the sample of wire you are testing. If you have wires of the same length and the same material, the thicker wire will need a larger tension for the same extension. If the wires are of the same material and thickness, but different lengths, the longer wire will have a larger extension for the same tension.

If you wish to compare the behaviour of different materials, you need to plot quantities that do not depend on the size of the sample of material tested.

Strain, symbol ε (the small Greek letter *epsilon*), is the extension divided by the original length:

$$\text{strain} = \frac{\text{extension}}{\text{original length}}$$

Strain accounts for the fact that samples stretch in proportion to their lengths. Strain has no units, since it is metres divided by metres.

A steel wire 2.0 m long, stretched to just below its breaking point, extends by 2.6 mm. Then

$$\text{strain} = (2.6 \times 10^{-3} \text{ m})/2.0 \text{ m} = 1.3 \times 10^{-3}$$

When comparing the behaviour of materials, stress, strain and stress–strain graphs are used, since these do not depend on the size of the sample tested, only on the properties of the material tested.

Producing a stress–strain graph for a wire

- When you stretch a wire elastically, the extensions are small, so you need special techniques to measure them. Use a test wire as long as possible and fix a vernier scale to it to measure the extension accurately. Hang the main scale on an identical reference wire (Figure 6.2). Measure the length and diameter of the test wire. Use a fixed weight to keep the reference wire taut.
- Measure the extension of the test wire for a range of tensions. For each reading, calculate the stress and the strain.
- Plot a graph of stress against strain and measure its slope.

 EYE PROTECTION MUST BE WORN

 FALLING MASSES

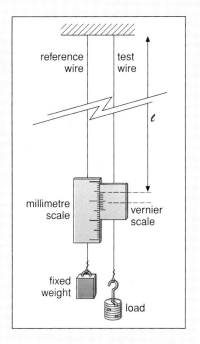

Figure 6.2 Measuring stress and strain for a wire

Stress–strain graphs

Stress–strain graphs are the standard way of comparing different materials under tension.

Figure 6.3 shows stress–strain graphs for copper, steel and polystyrene. All three graphs are straight lines at the beginning, showing that the strain is proportional to the stress, but each graph has a different slope. The dotted line on the graph is a line of constant stress. For each of the materials, the strain for this stress is different. The strain for polystyrene is the most, showing that it stretches a lot for a given stress; the strain for steel is the least. From this you can deduce that steel is the stiffest of the materials, since its strain is least for a given stress, and that polystyrene is the least stiff.

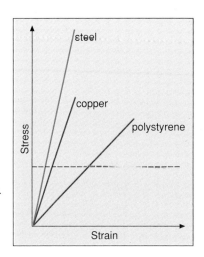

Figure 6.3 Stress–strain graphs

The Young modulus

The slope of the straight-line part of the stress–strain graph for a particular material is called the **Young modulus** of the material:

$$\text{Young modulus} = \frac{\text{stress}}{\text{strain}} \quad \text{or} \quad E = \frac{\sigma}{\varepsilon}$$

Young modulus is a measure of the stiffness of the material. A stiff material has a high Young modulus.

Stiffness is important for engineering materials, since for most applications it is important that the shape of a component changes very little when it is under stress. So engineering materials are often those with a high Young modulus. Obvious examples are metals, particularly steel (Table 6.1). For many consumer goods, stiffness is much less important. So you find flexible materials such as polystyrene being used for a wide range of items in which significant changes in shape in use do not matter.

Table 6.1 *Tensile strengths and strains at breaking*

Material	Ultimate tensile strength/MPa	Strain at breaking point	Young modulus/GPa
steel	250	~0.05	200
copper	150	~0.3	120
polystyrene	40	~0.03	35
nylon	70	~1	2
polyethene	20	~2	0.4

7 Inside the atom

Atoms have parts

The possibility that matter cannot be cut up into smaller and smaller pieces, but consists of indivisible particles called atoms, has been a subject for speculation since Greek and Roman times. The first clear evidence for the existence of atoms came from chemistry early in the nineteenth century. But final confirmation had to wait until a detailed study of radioactivity early in the twentieth century.

Protons, neutrons and electrons

The three principal parts of the atom are the proton, neutron and electron. The electron was the first to be investigated separately. As a result of J.J. Thomson's work in 1896 and Robert Millikan's in 1906, the electron was known to be part of all atoms; its mass and its negative charge were known. The proton has an equal and opposite charge to the electron, and the neutron is uncharged. The mass of the proton is about 1800 times the mass of an electron; the mass of a neutron is slightly greater still. Table 7.1 summarises these properties.

Table 7.1 *Properties of the proton, neutron and electron*

Property	Proton	Neutron	Electron
mass	1.7×10^{-27} kg 1 u (atomic mass unit)	1.7×10^{-27} kg 1 u	9.1×10^{-31} kg 1/1800 u
charge	$+1.6 \times 10^{-19}$ C	0	-1.6×10^{-19} C
description	a nucleon; part of the nucleus	a nucleon; part of the nucleus	in a cloud around the nucleus

Figure 7.1 Sir Ernest Rutherford

Little was known about the structure of atoms until, in 1911, Ernest Rutherford (Figure 7.1) asked two other researchers, Geiger and Marsden, to carry out an experiment. As you can read in the next chapter, certain atoms give out alpha (α) **particles**. At the time of Rutherford's experiment, these were known to be positive particles that are part of the helium atom. We know now that they consist of two protons and two neutrons.

Alpha (α) particle scattering

- Geiger and Marsden arranged to fire alpha particles at thin gold foil and detect them by a screen, which gave out a flash of light whenever it was hit by an alpha particle (Figure 7.2).
- By counting the flashes, they compared the number of alpha particles passing straight through with the numbers deflected through various angles.

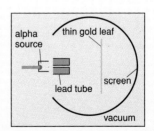

Figure 7.2 Alpha scattering apparatus

The nuclear atom

The results of the alpha particle scattering experiment were surprising. Geiger observed that the vast majority of the alpha particles are deflected very little as they travel through the gold foil, but a tiny minority are deflected through large angles. Figure 7.3 gives a representation of these observations.

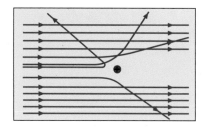

Figure 7.3   About 1 in 8000 alpha particles were deflected through greater than 90°

Rutherford knew that alpha particles had masses equal to those of light atoms. So whatever deflected the alpha particles would need to have more mass than a light atom. He knew that the negative charges, the electrons, had too little mass to deflect the alpha particles; so the deflection must be due to the positive charges in the atom. These positive charges must have comparatively large distances between them to account for the fact that most alpha particles are undeflected.

Rutherford found the solution to these puzzles in the nuclear atom. He suggested that most of the mass of the atom is concentrated in a tiny positively charged centre called the **nucleus**. We now know that the nucleus contains both the protons and neutrons, and that the electrons form a cloud in the 'space' of the atom.

Atomic and nuclear sizes

Thin gold foil (Figure 7.4) can be typically 1/1000th millimetre ($= 10^{-6}$ m $= 1$ µm) thick. At this thickness, the foil is about 3000 atoms thick – the diameter of a gold atom is about 0.3×10^{-9} m ($= 0.3$ nm). The nucleus is more than 10 000 times smaller still – less than 10^{-14} m in diameter. If the gold atom were the same size as this page, the nucleus would be 100 times smaller than a single full stop.

Figure 7.4   Thin gold foil

Describing atoms

An atom's **proton number**, symbol Z, is the number of protons in an atom. In a neutral atom, the number of protons in the nucleus is equal to the number of electrons round the outside. All the atoms of a particular element have the same proton number, so the proton number of an atom identifies which element it is. The proton number is sometimes called the **atomic number**.

The proton number of carbon is 6; a neutral carbon atom has six protons and six electrons.

Protons and neutrons are **nucleons**. The **nucleon number**, symbol A, of an atom is the total number of protons and neutrons in the nucleus of that atom. The protons and neutrons are the most massive particles in an atom, and they both have approximately the same mass. So the nucleon number gives an approximate indication of the mass of an atom. For this reason, the nucleon number is sometimes called the **mass number**. Both the nucleon number and the proton number are integers (whole numbers).

To find the number, N, of neutrons in an atom, subtract the proton number from the nucleon number. For example, gold (symbol Au) has a proton number of 79 and a mass number of 197. So for gold:

$$N = A - Z = 197 - 79 = 118$$

$^{197}_{79}$Au is a shorthand way of indicating the proton and nucleon numbers.

Isotopes

A nucleus with a stated proton number and neutron number is called a nuclide. An **isotope** of a nuclide is another nuclide with the same proton number but a different neutron number. $^{12}_{6}$C and $^{14}_{6}$C are both isotopes of carbon. They have the same number of protons, but $^{14}_{6}$C has two more neutrons than $^{12}_{6}$C. The proton number determines the arrangement of the electrons around the nucleus, and so decides the chemical properties of an atom. So all isotopes of a nuclide have the same chemical properties because they have the same proton number. They have different atomic masses, and so have different densities.

The unified mass unit

Accurate measurement of atomic mass is based on the carbon-12 atom, $^{12}_{6}$C. The **unified mass unit**, u, is defined as one-twelfth of the mass of a carbon-12 atom. Its value is u $= 1.66 \times 10^{-27}$ kg. The mass of a hydrogen atom is 1.0079 u. Alternatively, you may say that the **relative atomic mass** of hydrogen is 1.0079.

8 Ionising radiations

Conducting air

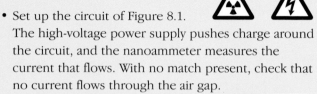

- Set up the circuit of Figure 8.1. The high-voltage power supply pushes charge around the circuit, and the nanoammeter measures the current that flows. With no match present, check that no current flows through the air gap.
- Now hold a match flame underneath the air gap and observe the meter.
- Then bring an americium radioactive source to the air gap and observe the meter.

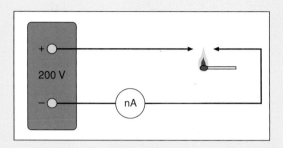

Figure 8.1   Measuring current through an air gap

Ionising air

When you hold a flame under the air gap in the circuit of Figure 8.1, the meter indicates that a current is flowing. The flame is causing the air to conduct. When you hold the radioactive source near the gap, the same thing happens and the air conducts.

The flame **ionises** the air. It gives atoms in the air sufficient energy to release electrons. This produces free negatively charged electrons and free positively charged ions, which conduct a current. The radiation from the americium also ionises the air; so it is called ionising radiation. The radiation released by the americium is called **alpha (α) radiation**.

Investigating alpha (α) radiation

- The ionisation chamber is an enclosed air gap that you can use to investigate radiation. Any radiation that gets in to the chamber and ionises the air enables a current to flow and be detected by the meter.
- Check that the americium source produces an ionisation current when you hold it near the gauze (Figure 8.2). Then move the source further away from the gauze until the current stops, so that you can find the distance that the alpha radiation can travel through air.
- Then hold the source close to the gauze. Put thin pieces of paper between the source and the gauze to investigate the distance that alpha radiation can travel through paper.

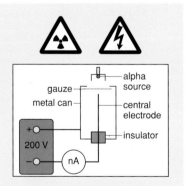

Figure 8.2   Detecting the ions produced by alpha radiation

The range of alpha radiation

Alpha radiation is heavily ionising – it produces many ions per millimetre along its path. But the range of alpha radiation is limited. It is stopped by 5 – 6 cm of air, or by thin paper.

The mechanism of alpha decay

You read in Chapter 7 that alpha particles consist of two protons and two neutrons. This is the same as the nucleus of the helium-4 nuclide ($^4_2$He). Americium decays by emitting an alpha particle. The proton number decreases by 2 and the nucleon number decreases by 4. The atom becomes neptunium; it is no longer americium. This equation shows the decay:

$$^{241}_{95}\text{Am} \rightarrow \, ^{237}_{93}\text{Np} \, + \, ^4_2\alpha$$

Neptunium decays by a further alpha decay to protactinium-233:

$$^{237}_{93}\text{Np} \rightarrow \, ^{233}_{91}\text{Pa} \, + \, ^4_2\alpha$$

When, at the end of its path, an alpha particle stops, it picks up two electrons and becomes a helium atom. Alpha decay within the Earth is responsible for the presence of helium in natural gas deposits.

The Geiger–Müller tube

The ionisation chamber needs a large number of ions to be produced for a measurable current. A Geiger–Müller (GM) tube (Figure 8.3) will detect each ionising event inside the tube, whether the event involves a single pair of ions, or many ions. For each ionising event, a pulse of current passes through the tube and is recorded by the attached counter. GM tubes are poor detectors of alpha radiation, because even the thin end window stops many alpha particles. But GM tubes can detect more penetrating, but less ionising, radiations that ionisation chambers are not able to detect.

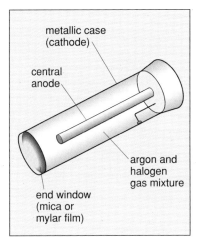

Figure 8.3   A Geiger–Müller tube

Investigating beta-minus (β-) radiation

- Strontium-90 is a beta-minus emitter. Use a source-handling tool to mount a strontium-90 source near the GM tube and measure the count rate.
- For a range of distances from the tube, measure the count rate. Plot a graph of count rate against distance.
- Fix the beta-minus source 3 cm from the GM tube and measure the count rate (Figure 8.4).
- Insert a piece of paper between the source and the tube, and measure the new rate.
- Then insert a series of thin pieces of aluminium between the source and the tube. Plot a graph of count rate against number of pieces of aluminium.

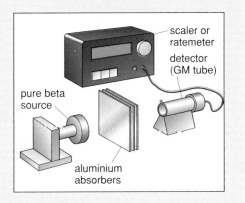

Figure 8.4   Investigating beta radiation

Properties of beta-minus (β-) radiation

Beta-minus (β-) radiation is much less heavily ionising than alpha radiation, and so is very difficult to detect with an ionisation chamber. However, beta-minus radiation will travel more than 30 cm through air and through several millimetres of aluminium.

In beta-minus decay, a neutron in the nucleus splits up into a proton plus an electron. The proton stays in the nucleus; the electron is ejected at high speed – it is a beta-minus particle. Beta-minus particles are fast electrons that have been emitted from the nucleus.

When beta-minus decay occurs, the number of nucleons stays the same. The number of protons goes up by 1, the number of neutrons goes down by 1 and an electron is emitted. Strontium-90 becomes yttrium-90, as the equation shows:

$$^{90}_{38}Sr \rightarrow \; ^{90}_{39}Y \; + \; ^{\;\;0}_{-1}\beta$$

Yttrium-90 decays by a further beta-minus decay to potassium-90:

$$^{90}_{39}Y \rightarrow \; ^{90}_{40}K \; + \; ^{\;\;0}_{-1}\beta$$

Beta-plus (β^+) decay

Another type of decay, beta-plus (β^+) decay, occurs rarely in Nature, but more frequently in man-made radionuclides. In beta-plus decay, a proton in the nucleus splits up into a neutron plus a positron. The neutron remains; the beta-plus particle is ejected at high speed.

When beta-plus decay occurs, the number of nucleons stays the same. The number of neutrons goes up by 1, the number of protons goes down by 1 and a positron is emitted.

Carbon-11 decays by beta-plus decay to boron-11, as the equation shows:

$$^{11}_{6}C \rightarrow \; ^{11}_{5}B \; + \; ^{0}_{1}\beta$$

You will find more details about both types of beta decay in the 'Particle Physics' option in Module 4.

Gamma (γ) radiation

After emitting alpha or beta radiation, a nucleus may have surplus energy. Often it gives out this energy by emitting electromagnetic radiation. These photons of radiation are called **gamma (γ) rays**. You can read more about photons in Chapter 27.

Investigating gamma radiation

- Use the arrangement in figure 8.4 to measure the count rate at different distances from a cobalt-60 gamma source.
- Then use a source-handling tool to mount the source 8 cm from the tube and measure the count rate for a range of thicknesses of lead absorbers between the source and the tube.

Properties of gamma radiation

The gamma radiation from a source is a stream of electromagnetic photons. The photons ionise when they react drastically with matter along the path, knocking a single electron from an atom and therefore producing a single ion pair. The ejected electron produces further ion pairs as it collides with other atoms. When a gamma photon ionises an atom, the number of photons decreases, but the remaining photons are unchanged. Gamma radiation causes relatively little ionisation per millimetre of its path. Because it interacts so little, it has a large range. High-energy gamma radiation is attenuated (reduced in strength), but not stopped, by several centimetres of lead.

Deflecting radiation with magnetic fields

- Use a source-handling tool to mount a beta source 10 cm from a GM tube and then bring up a magnet as shown in Figure 8.5. Note the change in the count.
- Then move the GM tube into a position like that shown by the dotted lines to find the deflected particles.
- Repeat the experiment with alpha and gamma sources in turn.

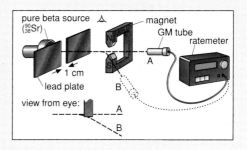

Figure 8.5   Deflecting beta radiation

Deflecting radiations in fields

Alpha and beta radiation both have electric charge; they can be deflected by both electric and magnetic fields. Gamma radiation is uncharged and cannot be so deflected.

Figure 8.6 shows the deflections of the radiations in a magnetic field. You need to use Fleming's left-hand rule to check the deflection of the particles. Both alpha and beta-plus are positive. The direction of travel is the direction of the current. They are deflected upwards. Beta-minus radiation is deflected in the opposite direction. Alpha particles are so much more massive than beta particles that their deflection is hardly noticeable; their deflection on the diagram is greatly exaggerated.

Similarly, alpha and beta radiation can be deflected by electric fields, as shown in Figure 8.7. Alpha and beta-plus are attracted to the negative plate; beta-minus is attracted to the positive plate. Again, the deflection of the alpha particles is tiny compared to that of the beta radiation, and is exaggerated in the diagram to make it visible. Table 8.1 summarises the properties of alpha, beta-minus, beta-plus and gamma radiation.

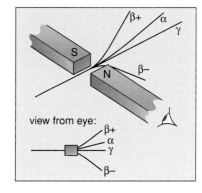

Figure 8.6   Behaviour of radiations in a magnetic field

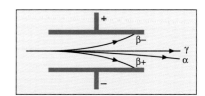

Figure 8.7   Electric deflection

Property	Alpha (α)	Beta-minus (β-)	Beta-plus (β+)	Gamma (γ)
charge	+2	−1	+1	0
rest mass	4 u	1/1800 u	1/1800 u	0
penetration	5 cm air; thin paper	30 cm air; few mm Al	annihilated on interaction with an electron	long way; keeps going through Pb
nature	helium nucleus	electron	positron	e.m. wave
ionising	heavily	light		a single ion pair on interaction

Table 8.1   *Summary of the properties of the different radiations*

9 Nuclear stability

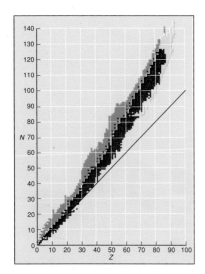

Figure 9.1   N–Z curve

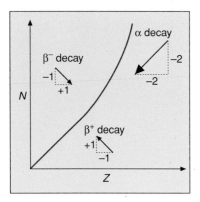

Figure 9.2   Radioactive decay brings the nuclide plot closer to the trend line

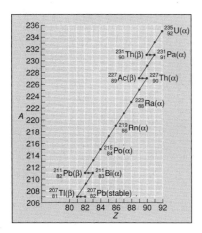

Figure 9.3   Decay chain

The N–Z curve

If you plot a graph of the numbers of neutrons N against the proton numbers Z for all nuclides, you see a distinct pattern. For the nuclides with lower proton numbers, the number of neutrons is similar to the number of protons. The nuclides are clustered around the line $N = Z$. As the proton number increases, the number of neutrons exceeds the number of protons. The plots of the nuclides form the N–Z trend line shown in Figure 9.1.

There are no plots a long way from the trend line. This implies that such nuclides are never formed or are not stable. In general, nuclide plots that are some way from the trend line come closer to the trend line when they decay, ie they tend to become more stable. Those nuclides which are at the very top of the trend line are unstable and they decay down the trend line.

When alpha decay occurs, both N and Z decrease by 2. This causes the atom to move diagonally down in the general direction of the origin, as Figure 9.2 shows.

With beta-minus decay, N decreases by 1 and Z increases by 1. The atom moves diagonally down, towards the trend line. With beta-plus decay, N increases by 1 and Z decreases by 1. The atom moves diagonally up, towards the trend line.

Figure 9.3 shows a typical sequence of decays by which a large nuclide decays along the trend line from a massive nuclide to a smaller one. Use the data to plot an N–Z curve for this decay sequence.

Binding energy

If you assemble a small nuclide out of separate protons and electrons, energy is released. This energy is called the **binding energy**. If you want to separate a nucleus again into the separate particles, you have to supply this energy to the nucleus.

Like all energy, the binding energy has mass m, given by the formula:

$$m = \frac{E}{c^2}$$

where E is the energy and c is the speed of light. This means that you can find the mass equivalent to the binding energy by subtracting the mass of a nucleus from the total mass of the separate particles. The difference is called the **mass defect**.

For example, the mass of a proton is 1.007 276 u and the mass of a neutron is 1.008 665 u. Two protons and two neutrons together make a helium nucleus (an alpha particle), which has a mass of 4.002 603 u. So we can work out the mass defect and find the binding energy, as follows:

mass of protons	$= 2 \times 1.007\ 276$ u	$= 2.014\ 552$ u
mass of neutrons	$= 2 \times 1.008\ 665$ u	$= 2.017\ 330$ u
total mass of protons plus neutrons		$= 4.031\ 882$ u
mass of nucleus		$= 4.002\ 603$ u
mass defect		$= 0.029\ 279$ u
		$= 0.029\ 279 \times 1.66 \times 10^{-27}$ kg
		$= 4.86 \times 10^{-29}$ kg

$$\text{binding energy of helium nucleus } E = mc^2$$
$$= 4.86 \times 10^{-29} \text{ kg} \times (3 \times 10^8 \text{ m s}^{-1})^2$$
$$= 4.4 \times 10^{-12} \text{ J}$$

Binding energy per nucleon

If you divide the binding energy of a nuclide by the number of nucleons in that nuclide, you get the binding energy per nucleon. Figure 9.4 shows the binding energy per nucleon plotted against mass number for nuclides of different mass numbers. This shows how much energy is given out per nucleon for a given mass number. The most stable nuclides are those with the most binding energy per nucleon; but you can see that the binding energy per nucleon changes relatively little from mass number 60 to mass number 100.

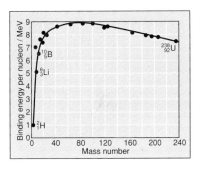

Figure 9.4   Binding energy per nucleon

Fusion and fission

Fusion means *joining together*. If you join together light nuclei, large amounts of energy are released as the binding energy per nucleon increases. In *Thermal Physics* you can read about nuclear fusion in the core of stars, where protons are joining together to make helium nuclei, releasing vast amounts of energy. Large investments are being made jointly by European countries in the JET project (Figure 9.5) to research into nuclear fusion as a practicable future power source. This centres around colliding two deuterium nuclei ($_1^2$H) to make helium.

Fission means *splitting up*. Nuclear fission already powers present-day nuclear power stations. In this, large nuclides with mass numbers over 200, usually uranium or plutonium, are bombarded with neutrons to split them into nuclides with mass numbers of around 80. The binding energy per nucleon increases, meaning that energy is released. Again, you can read more about this in *Thermal Physics*.

Figure 9.5   The Joint European Torus – a test-bed for nuclear fusion

Measuring background radiation

- Set up a GM tube and counter with no source within 5 m.
- Measure the counts in one minute, ten times in a row.
- Display your results as a histogram.

Background radiation

Radiation is around us all the time, in the background. It is mainly due to Nature but partly due to human activity. Naturally occurring radio-isotopes – those which exist without human intervention – contribute to this **background radiation**. The biggest source of these is in uranium deposits in the ground, which in turn produce other isotopes that decay. A common naturally occurring radio-isotope is radon gas, which spreads throughout the ground and is part of the air we breathe. Next to smoking it is the biggest cause of lung cancer. The other big natural contributor to background radiation comes from cosmic rays – mostly fast-moving nuclei from outer space. They bombard, and are mostly absorbed by, the atmosphere, sending showers of particles to the Earth's surface.

Very large nuclei have far more neutrons than protons, so the medium-mass fragments produced in nuclear fission, for instance in nuclear reactors or the explosion of nuclear weapons, have too many neutrons for stability. Thus they are beta-minus emitters and some also emit gamma rays. Useful radio-nuclides are obtained by chemical processing of discharged nuclear fuel. Other useful radio-nuclides can be produced by bombarding atoms with the immense numbers of neutrons in a reactor. As neutrons are uncharged, they are easily captured by many nuclei. Machines such as cyclotrons can bombard materials with protons, deuterons or heavier nuclei.

Radioactivity produced by human activity is responsible for less than 1% of background radiation, but it is very useful, particularly to medicine, where radioactivity is used in the diagnosis and treatment of illness. You can read more about this in Module 3.

Random decay

Figure 10.1 shows a histogram of a large number of one-minute background counts. The fluctuation in count occurs because all radioactive decay is **random** – there is no way of predicting when a particular nucleus will decay. But when there are large numbers involved, there are general statistical patterns.

If you take a sample of radioactive material, the activity will slowly decline, because as the nuclei decay there are fewer and fewer nuclei left that can decay. This general decline in the level of activity can be modelled by throwing dice, where each die represents a nucleus.

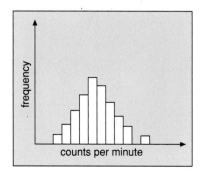

Figure 10.1 A histogram of background counts

Throwing dice

- Take 100 dice. Throw them all together and remove those which show a six. Stack these in a line.
- Then throw the remaining dice, and again remove those which show a six. Stack these in a line next to the first one. Repeat until all the dice are removed.
- Produce graphs of number remaining for each throw and number removed for each throw.

The decay equation

The throw of one die is, like radioactivity, random. But a pattern emerges if you throw a large number. On average, each die will show a six once in every six throws. You cannot predict which throw will produce a six. But if you throw 100 dice and remove those which show a six, you will remove on average about 16 dice after the first throw. Figure 10.2 shows graphs for the number of dice remaining and the number of dice removed if you continue this process.

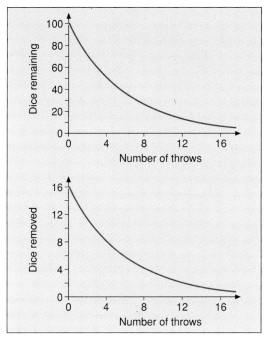

Figure 10.2   Modelling radioactive decay with 100 dice

On any one occasion, the number showing a six, N_6, is proportional to the total number of dice thrown, N:

$$N_6 \propto N \qquad \text{or} \qquad N_6 = \text{constant} \times N$$

In this case the constant would be 1/6.

Similarly, for radioactive atoms, the number that decay in an instant is proportional to the total number N at the begining of that instant.

The rate of change of N is dN/dt, where t is time. dN/dt is negative, because N is decreasing with time. So we can write

$$dN/dt = -\lambda N$$

where N is the number of nuclei at that instant and λ (the Greek letter *lambda*) is the **decay constant**; λ has units second^{-1}, and represents the proportion of N that decays in one second.

If the average rate of decay for 72 nuclei is 12 s^{-1}, then $dN/dt = -12$ for $N = 72$. So

$$dN/dt = -\lambda N$$

$$-12 \text{ s}^{-1} = -\lambda \times 72$$

$$\lambda = 1/6 \text{ s}^{-1}$$

The rate of decay dN/dt is called the activity. It is measured in counts per second, called the becquerel (Bq). As the decay proceeds, N is smaller at the start of each successive time interval. So the magnitude of dN/dt also gets smaller and smaller as the decay proceeds.

The decay constant λ has a different value for each radioactive isotope, because each isotope decays at a different rate. If the decay is rapid, λ is large. If the decay is slow, λ is small. Note that λ is constant for the isotope and does not vary during the decay. The rate changes because N changes.

Measuring half-life

- Protactinium-234 is a beta-minus emitter; a compound of it is soluble in organic solvent. It is generated in a water-based solution in the protactinium generator. Shake the generator gently to dissolve the protactinium compound from the water-based liquid, stand the generator next to the GM tube and allow the organic solvent to float to the top of the water (Figure 10.3).
- After the liquids have stabilised, start the counter and record the count every 3 s for 5 min.
- Plot a graph of the count rate against time. From this, determine the time for half the protactinium in the top layer to decay.

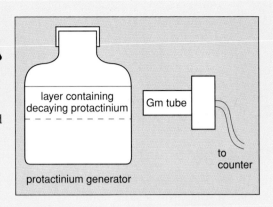

Figure 10.3　*Measuring the decay of protactinium dissolved in the top liquid layer*

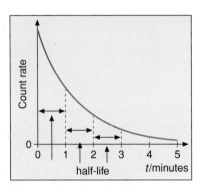

Figure 10.4　*Decay graph*

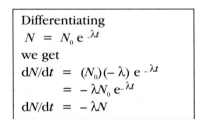

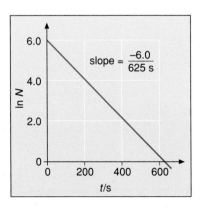

Figure 10.5　*Graph of ln N against t*

Half-life

However large the radioactive sample, experiment shows that for any particular isotope the average time for half of the atoms of one isotope to decay is constant. This time is called the **half-life**. The half-life of the isotope in Figure 10.4 is about one minute. You can measure half-life directly from a count–time graph, but there is a mathematically more elegant way if you know the equation of this graph.

The decay curve is an **exponential decay**. It is described by the equation:

$$N = N_0 e^{-\lambda t} \quad \text{which is the same as} \quad N = N_0/e^{\lambda t}$$

The number N of undecayed atoms left after time t is proportional to the number N_0 you started with. $e^{\lambda t}$ increases with time because t is increasing. So the number left decreases with time. The box shows that this is compatible with the equation

$$dN/dt = -\lambda N$$

If you take natural logarithms of both sides of the equation $N = N_0 e^{-\lambda t}$, you get

$$\ln N = \ln N_0 - \lambda t \quad \text{or} \quad \ln N = -\lambda t + \ln N_0$$

This is of the form $y = mx + c$. So a graph of $\ln N$ against t will have slope $-\lambda$.

Practice question 10.2 shows the connection between the half-life and the decay constant:

$$t_{1/2} = (\ln 2)/\lambda$$

Figure 10.5 is a graph of $\ln N$ against t for the experiment with protactinium. We can find the half-life of protactinium as follows:

$$\text{slope} = -\lambda = -6.0/(625\ \text{s})$$

and therefore

$$\lambda = 9.68 \times 10^{-3}\ \text{s}^{-1}$$

which gives a half-life of

$$t_{1/2} = (\ln 2)/\lambda = 0.693/(9.68 \times 10^{-3}\ \text{s}^{-1})$$

$$t_{1/2} = 72\ \text{s}$$

Oscillations and waves

And sea waves get much bigger than this!

Observing repeating motions

• Observe the systems shown in Figure 11.1. Set them going quickly, and then slowly.

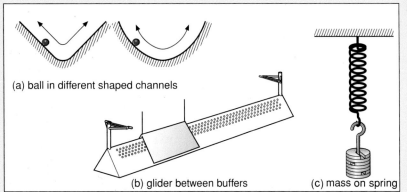

Figure 11.1   Systems that can move to and fro

(a) ball in different shaped channels

(b) glider between buffers   (c) mass on spring

• Make the movements large and then small.
• What do you observe?

Oscillations

Many systems have repeated movements. But the motion of some systems is regular, and that of other systems is irregular. The swings of a particular pendulum all take the same time, however fast the pendulum is swinging. But the to-and-fro motion of a glider bouncing between the ends of an air track depends on the speed of the glider.

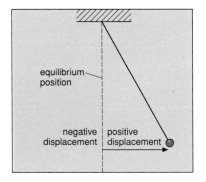

Figure 11.2   The displacement of this pendulum is positive

The motion of your legs as you walk steadily, the vibrations of a mechanical road digger, the movements of piano strings – these are all repeating motions that are regular. Movements like these are particularly interesting and useful. Since they are regular, you can use them for clocks. Regular movements like these are called **oscillations**. The bodies that oscillate move backwards and forwards either side of their **equilibrium position**, the position in which the resultant force on them is zero, and in which they would be at rest if not oscillating.

At any instant during an oscillation, you can record the position of the body – its **displacement** – from its equilibrium position. When a body is oscillating, it goes either side of its equilibrium position. You can use positive values to indicate displacements on one side, and negative values to indicate displacements in the opposite direction, as Figure 11.2 shows. You can produce a **time trace**, which is a graph to show how the displacement of an oscillation varies with time.

Producing time traces

• Attach a pen to a metre rule clamped to a bench leg. Adjust the pen so that it writes on a piece of paper pulled underneath (Figure 11.3). Set the rule vibrating and pull the paper at constant speed to obtain a displacement–time graph for the vibrating rule.

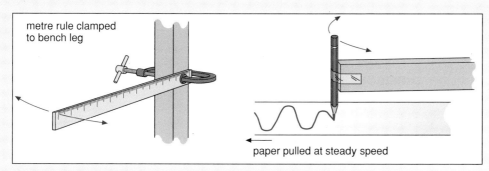

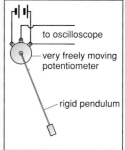

Figure 11.3   Producing a time trace for a vibrating metre rule

Figure 11.4   Producing a time trace for a pendulum

- The pendulum in Figure 11.4 swings from a potentiometer. The voltage from the circuit depends on the displacement. Set the pendulum swinging and use the oscilloscope to observe how the displacement varies with time. Sketch a graph for the motion.
- Set up a mass oscillating on the end of a spring as in Figure 11.5. Place a motion sensor connected to a computer below the oscillating mass. Use the computer to display a displacement–time graph for the oscillating mass.
- Compare the time traces for each of the above oscillations. What things do they have in common?

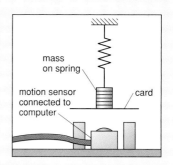

Figure 11.5   Using a motion sensor to produce a time trace

Amplitude, period and frequency

As Figure 11.6 shows, the **amplitude** of an oscillation is the maximum displacement from the equilibrium position. For each of the oscillating systems in the experiment, the amplitudes of oscillation decrease as the oscillations gradually die away. A complete movement of an oscillating system – from its equilibrium position, to a displacement in one direction, back to the equilibrium position, to a displacement in the reverse direction and finally back to its equilibrium position again – is called one **cycle**. The oscillating systems in the experiments above are regularly repeating. The time for one cycle, called the **period**, is constant. The period does not change when the amplitude decreases as the oscillations die away.

It is convenient to use the period to describe the rate of slow oscillations. The period of the pendulum of a grandfather clock is 2 s. But many oscillations are *very* quick, and if the period is short, it is more usual to describe the rate of oscillation by the number of complete oscillations per second – the **frequency**, measured in hertz (Hz). The frequency of the sounds you hear varies from about 30 Hz up to about 20 000 Hz – that is, from 30 to 20 000 oscillations per second (or 30 to 20 000 s^{-1}).

You can calculate the period from the frequency:

period = 1/frequency   or $T = 1/f$

For the top of the audible frequency range,

$T = 1/f = 1/(20\,000\ \text{Hz}) = 1/(20\,000\ \text{s}^{-1}) = 50\ \mu\text{s}$

Figure 11.6   As the oscillation dies away, the amplitude decreases

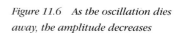

Simple harmonic motion

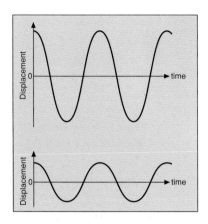

Figure 12.1   The period of oscillation is independent of amplitude

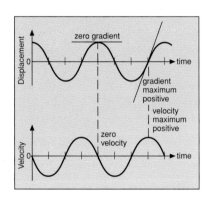

Figure 12.2   Displacement and velocity for an oscillating trolley

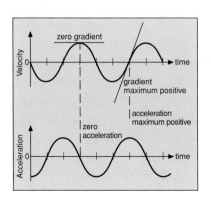

Figure 12.3   Velocity and acceleration for an oscillating trolley

Sinusoidal motion

Figure 12.1 shows time traces for a trolley tethered by springs. The period of these oscillations is independent of amplitude – it remains the same whether the trolley is making large oscillations, or small ones. Motion like this is called **simple harmonic motion (s.h.m.)**. Displacement–time graphs for simple harmonic motion all have a characteristic shape – called **sinusoidal**, the shape of a mathematical sine or cosine graph.

Velocity and displacement

You can deduce a velocity–time graph for simple harmonic motion from the gradient of a displacement–time graph. As Figure 12.2 shows, the gradient of the displacement–time graph is zero when the displacement is a maximum. The velocity is zero at these points. For a trolley between two springs, the velocity is zero for a moment at either end of the motion, where the displacement is maximum positive, or maximum negative.

The velocity is maximum positive, or maximum negative, when the displacement is zero – when the trolley is in the centre of the motion, moving fastest either to left or to right.

Acceleration and velocity

You can deduce the acceleration–time graph from the velocity–time graph. As Figure 12.3 shows, when the velocity is maximum, the gradient of the velocity–time graph is zero, and therefore the acceleration is zero. The acceleration is zero in the middle of the motion, when the velocity is maximum positive or maximum negative.

The acceleration is maximum, positive or negative, when the velocity is zero – when the trolley is momentarily stationary at the extremes of its motion.

Acceleration and displacement

Figure 12.4 puts Figures 12.2 and 12.3 together and shows the relationship between acceleration and displacement. The acceleration is zero when the displacement is zero – in the middle of the motion. The acceleration is large where the displacement is large, but to the left when the displacement is to the right. The acceleration is maximum to the left when the displacement is maximum to the right – and vice versa. The acceleration is always directed towards the equilibrium position.

The acceleration is proportional to the displacement, but in the opposite direction to the displacement. Mathematically:

$$\text{acceleration} \propto -\text{displacement} \qquad \text{or} \qquad a \propto -x$$

This relationship between acceleration and displacement produces simple harmonic motion. Often we write the s.h.m. equation as:

$$a = -\omega^2 x$$

(ω is the Greek letter *omega*). ω^2 is always positive, so the acceleration and the displacement are always of opposite sign. For reasons that you will see in the next chapter, ω is called the angular speed and, just as with circular motion, ω is related to the period by the equation

$$T = 2\pi/\omega$$

Force and displacement

You know that force is proportional to acceleration. And since acceleration is proportional to negative displacement, force must be proportional to negative displacement:

$$F \propto -x$$

You can define simple harmonic motion as the motion that occurs when a body has an acceleration (or a force) that is directly proportional to its displacement from a fixed point and is always directed towards that point.

For a trolley tethered between two springs, the force F is proportional to the displacement x. The force is always in the opposite direction to the displacement, so we can write:

$$F = -kx$$

where k is the spring constant. Since $F = ma$, where m is the mass and a is the acceleration, we can write

$$ma = -kx \quad \text{and so} \quad a = -(k/m)x$$

If you compare this equation with $a = -\omega^2 x$, you can see that

$$k/m = \omega^2 \quad \text{and so} \quad \omega = \sqrt{(k/m)}$$

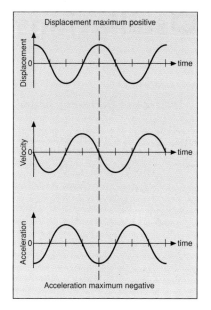

Figure 12.4 *Acceleration and displacement for an oscillating trolley*

Measuring ω for an oscillating trolley

- Measure the mass m of a trolley and then tether it between two springs as shown in Figure 12.5.

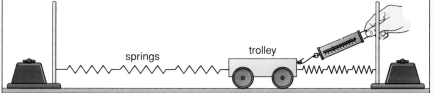

Figure 12.5 *Measuring the spring constant for a tethered trolley*

- Use a spring balance to measure the force needed to displace the trolley a measured distance from equilibrium.
- Calculate the spring constant k. From k/m calculate ω.
- Set the trolley oscillating and measure the period. Check the relationship between the period and ω.

Oscillations and circular motion

Circular paths and linear oscillators

- Tether a trolley between two springs and add mass to it to give it a period of about 2 s.
- Place the rotating disc centrally behind the trolley (Figure 13.1). Adjust the motor so that the time the peg takes to complete one orbit is the same as the period of the trolley.
- Pull the trolley to the left and release it as the peg gets furthest to the left.
- Compare the two motions.

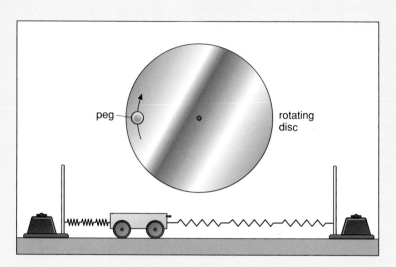

Figure 13.1   Keep the peg in step with the trolley

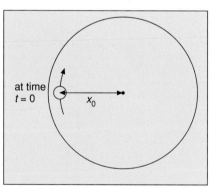

Figure 13.2   At time t = 0, the peg is a maximum distance to the left

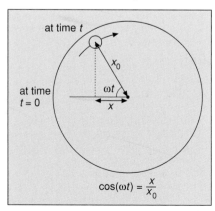

Figure 13.3   After a time t, the disc has rotated through an angle ωt

The shadow of a circular path

The peg on the disc in Figure 13.1 moves from side to side in step with the oscillating trolley. The two motions remain in phase (in step) with each other. The side-to-side motion of the trolley with its speed constantly increasing and decreasing is identical to the side-to-side motion of an object moving around a circular path at a constant speed. The angular speed ω for simple harmonic motion (s.h.m.) is the angular speed of circular motion that keeps in step with that s.h.m. The period T of the circular motion is the same as the period of the s.h.m. of the trolley, and is related to the angular velocity by the equation

$$T = 2\pi/\omega$$

Figure 13.2 shows the maximum displacement of the peg to the left, a distance x_0 from the centre of the disc. If the angular speed of the disc is ω, after a time t the disc has rotated through an angle ωt, as Figure 13.3 shows. The horizontal displacement is now x. So from the triangle in Figure 13.3:

$$\cos(\omega t) = x/x_0 \qquad \text{or} \qquad x = x_0 \cos(\omega t)$$

Figure 13.4 shows a graph of displacement x against time t. As you would expect, it is just like the time trace for s.h.m., since both vary sinusoidally with time. The maximum and minimum values of $\cos(\omega t)$ are $+1$ and -1; x can vary between x_0 and $-x_0$. So you can see that the amplitude of the motion is x_0.

The mathematics of s.h.m.

If you can differentiate, you can use this to find the equations for velocity v and acceleration a from the equation for the displacement x. Since

$x = x_0 \cos(\omega t)$

then

$v = \mathrm{d}x/\mathrm{d}t = -\omega x_0 \sin(\omega t)$

and

$a = \mathrm{d}v/\mathrm{d}t = -\omega^2 x_0 \cos(\omega t)$

These are the equations of the three graphs shown in Figure 12.4 in the last chapter. Since

$a = -\omega^2 x_0 \cos(\omega t)$

and

$x = x_0 \cos(\omega t)$

then

$a = -\omega^2 x$

This is the defining equation for s.h.m.
Since the values of both sine and cosine vary between $+1$ and -1, the maximum velocity is ωx_0 and the maximum acceleration is $\omega^2 x_0$.

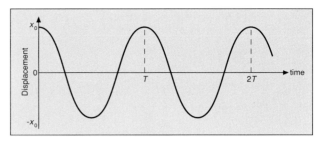

Figure 13.4   Horizontal displacement of the peg

Phase angles

Imagine two systems that are rotating or oscillating exactly in step. The displacement–time graphs for both of these oscillations would look like Figure 13.4 (though the graphs might have different amplitudes). These two objects are like two friendly runners on a circular track. At all times they are at exactly the same point as each other. These two objects are said to be **in phase**.

Figure 13.5 shows graphs for two runners who wish to keep as far apart as possible. They remain opposite each other on the track by moving around it at the same speed. The time traces are the same as those of two oscillators that are half an oscillation apart. These are exactly **out of phase** with each other or **in antiphase**. The phase angle difference between them is π radians (a straight line across the centre of the circle).

A phase difference of $\pi/2$ radians is shown in Figure 13.6

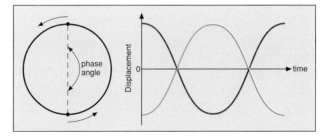

Figure 13.5   Moving in antiphase

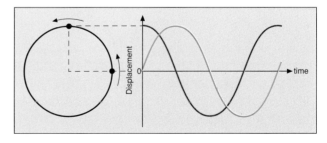

Figure 13.6   A phase difference of $\pi/2$ radians

14 Experimental study of simple harmonic motion

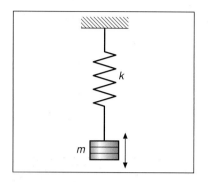

Figure 14.1 Vertical oscillation

Period for a mass – spring system

In Chapter 12 you learned that the angular speed ω for a trolley tethered between two springs depends on the mass of the trolley m and the spring constant of the spring system k:

$$\omega = \sqrt{(k/m)}$$

Since the period $T = 2\pi/\omega$, then

$$T = 2\pi\sqrt{\frac{m}{k}}$$

You can investigate experimentally how the period for a mass oscillating vertically on the end of a spring depends on k and m.

Another mass – spring system

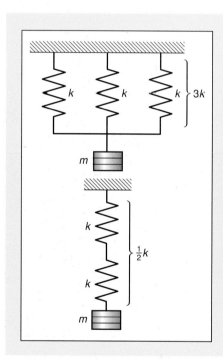

- Find the average spring constant of several identical springs. Use one of the springs and determine the period of oscillation of a known mass suspended from it (Figure 14.1). Time at least ten oscillations to increase the accuracy of your readings.
- Repeat your readings.
- Vary the mass and record a set of corresponding readings of mass m and period T. Plot a graph of T against $\sqrt{m}$. What relationship do you expect to find?
- Attach a mass of 500 g in turn to different spring combinations (Figure 14.2) and record the period T together with the spring constant k of the combination used. Plot a graph of T against $1/\sqrt{k}$. What do you expect to find?
- Using all your results, plot a graph of T against $\sqrt{(m/k)}$ and measure the gradient.

Figure 14.2 Producing different spring constants

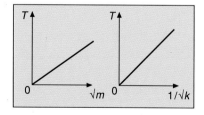

Figure 14.3 How mass and spring constant affect period

Analysis of results

For a mass oscillating at the end of a spring, graphs of period against $\sqrt{m}$ and period against $1/\sqrt{k}$ are straight lines through the origin (Figure 14.3). This shows that the period is proportional to the square root of the mass and inversely proportional to the square root of the spring constant, ie

$$T \propto \sqrt{(m/k)}$$

As you might expect, the constant of proportionality in this equation is 2π, so

$$T = 2\pi\sqrt{(m/k)}$$

just like the trolley oscillating between two springs.

A simple pendulum

- The motion of a pendulum is simple harmonic only when the amplitude of swing is small – less than about a sixth of the length of the pendulum (Figure 14.4).
- For small-angle swings, the period might depend on (a) the mass of the bob and/or (b) the length of the string. Predict how each of these variables affects the period.
- Carry out an experiment to test your prediction. Change only one variable at a time, and use a graph to show how period depends on the other variable.

Figure 14.4   Pendulum oscillations are simple harmonic only for small-angle swings

Period equation

For small-angle swings, the period of a pendulum of length l is given by

$$T = 2\pi\sqrt{(l/g)}$$

This shows that the period depends only on the length l of the pendulum and g, the acceleration of gravity. A graph of T against $\sqrt{l}$ will be a straight line through the origin with gradient $2\pi/\sqrt{g}$. You can use this graph to calculate a value for the acceleration of gravity.

Use of a pendulum in time-keeping

Grandfather clocks like that in Figure 14.5 are often fitted with a *seconds* pendulum, which advances the mechanism twice an oscillation at 1 s intervals. The period of such a pendulum is therefore 2 s.

But what must be the length of this pendulum? Using $T = 2\pi\sqrt{(l/g)}$ gives

$$l = (T/2\pi)^2 g = T^2 g/4\pi^2 = [(2\text{ s})^2 \times 9.8\text{ m s}^{-2}]/(4 \times \pi^2) = 0.99\text{ m}$$

This accounts for the height of such clocks, as their casings must be sufficiently long to house the pendulum. They are sometimes known as long-case clocks.

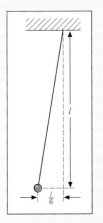

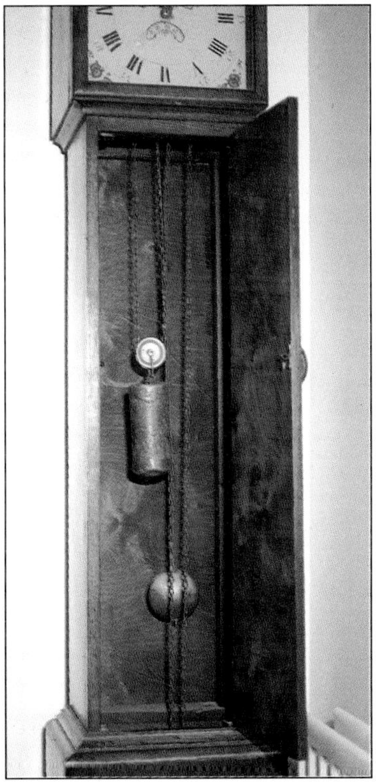

Figure 14.5   A long-case clock

Why is the period of s.h.m. constant?

For a long time, clocks used pendulums to keep time. Nowadays many clocks use a mass–spring system. Most modern clocks and wristwatches rely on a quartz crystal, where its own mass oscillates under its own springiness. In all these clocks, simple harmonic motion provides good time-keeping because the period is independent of the amplitude of oscillation. Think about why this is so.

If you double the amplitude of s.h.m., the period stays the same. The body has to travel twice the distance in the same time as before. Its average speed is doubled. This doubled speed is achieved in the same time, so the body has twice the average acceleration and twice the average resultant force acting on it, ie double the amplitude leads to double the maximum acceleration and double the force. The good time-keeping that s.h.m. provides is because force and acceleration are proportional to displacement.

15 | Mechanical resonance

Natural frequency

When you give a small displacement to a system that can oscillate, it oscillates at its own frequency. This is the oscillator's **natural frequency**.

Forced oscillations

- Hang 200 g from a spring and take sufficient readings to find the natural frequency of this system.
- Attach the spring and mass to the vibration generator as shown in Figure 15.1. Set the signal generator to produce sinusoidal waves and use a meter to measure its output frequency.
- Observe the mass's motion as you slowly increase the output frequency from well below the natural frequency of the mass – spring system to well above it. What do you expect to happen to the oscillations?
- Repeat the experiment for a different oscillating mass.

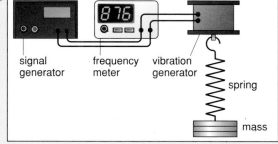

Figure 15.1   The vibrator causes the mass to oscillate

Resonance

The vibration generator is driving the mass – spring system and forcing it to oscillate. Forced oscillations are taking place. At all times, the driven system (the oscillating mass) oscillates at the frequency of the driver (the vibration generator). When the driving frequency is equal to the natural frequency of the driven system, large-amplitude, even violent, oscillations may result. This effect is called **resonance**. Resonance occurs when the driving frequency is equal to the natural frequency of the system you are driving.

Resonance curves

- Using the apparatus of Figure 15.1, record the maximum amplitude of the oscillating mass for a range of driver frequencies either side of resonance.
- Plot a graph of maximum amplitude against driver frequency.
- Repeat the experiment with the oscillating mass immersed in a beaker of water to provide some resistance to its motion. Repeat the measurements of maximum amplitude of oscillation for the same range of driver frequencies.
- Draw a second resonance curve on the same axes.
- How do the two graphs compare?

The effects of damping

Air resistance provides forces that reduce the amplitude of oscillations. This effect is called **damping**. For low damping, the resonance curve is sharp, and peaks when the driving frequency equals the system's natural frequency, as Figure 15.2 shows. The main effects of increased damping are to reduce the maximum amplitude of the driven system and to make resonance less noticeable. Increasing damping reduces the sharpness of the resonance curve – the peak becomes lower and wider.

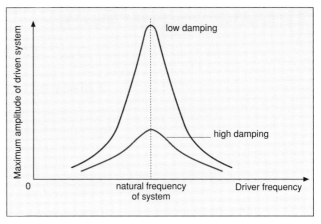

Figure 15.2   Resonance curves

Examples of mechanical resonance

There are many everyday situations that involve mechanical resonance. Some of these are useful, while others can be destructive and need to be avoided. In wind instruments, for example, sound is produced as a result of resonance (Figure 15.3). The vibrations of a small reed forces the molecules in an air column to vibrate.

Have you ever wondered why you find walking at one speed less tiring than walking at any other? Each of your legs is effectively a pendulum. The mass is not concentrated at a single point, so you cannot use a simple equation to find the period. But you can measure the natural frequency of your legs by standing on one leg and allowing your other leg to swing freely. Measure its natural frequency of oscillation and try to move your legs at this rate next time you go for a walk.

Figure 15.3   Resonance effects can be pleasing

Destructive resonance occurred in some early suspension bridges, which were subject to catastrophic failures when winds blowing past the structure caused oscillations at the natural frequency. Figure 15.4 shows the result of failing to prevent the frequency of these wind-induced oscillations matching the natural frequency of the bridge. Nowadays, engineers test models of such structures in wind tunnels before they are constructed, and try to modify the bridge to reduce the effects of resonance.

The parts of any machine containing a motor or an engine are subjected to periodic driving forces. Their design and construction must take account of this. Engineers try to ensure that the natural frequencies of the various parts of a car or an aeroplane are different from any periodic driving forces that the vehicle may experience during motion.

Figure 15.4   Resonance effects can be disastrous

Travelling waves

Pulses and waves

If you throw a stone into a pond, ripples spread out from where the stone hit. Disturbances like this die out; they are called wave pulses, because they last for a short time. If you want to produce continuous waves, you need to make repeated disturbances. The simplest sort of waves come from disturbances that are sinusoidal — from simple harmonic motion.

Observing waves

- Set up a ripple tank with a single dipper in the water (Figure 16.1). Tap the dipper and observe the shape of the ripples on the screen. Then use the vibrator to make continuous waves. Observe how the amplitude of the waves changes as the waves get further from their source.
- Connect a large loudspeaker to a signal generator producing a low-frequency signal. Listen to the sound. Place a lighted candle close to the centre of the loudspeaker and observe the movement of its flame (Figure 16.2). Move the candle further away and repeat the experiment. What do you observe?
- In a darkened room, connect a power supply to a small lamp. Hold a piece of paper near to the lamp and observe how brightly it is illuminated. Predict the illumination if you increase the distance between the paper and the lamp. Then test your prediction.

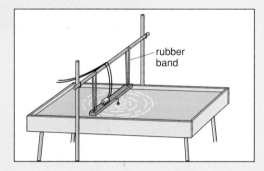

Figure 16.1   The moving dipper produces waves

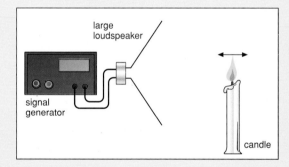

Figure 16.2   Observe the flickering flame

Energy and information

It is easy to observe the disturbances involved in water waves and sound waves. But the light emitted by the lamp is also a wave – an **electromagnetic wave** with electrical and magnetic disturbances. All these waves travel out from the source that makes them. For this reason, they are called **travelling waves** or **progressive waves**. Travelling waves from the Sun convey energy to the Earth. But they also give us information about the Sun – we can tell how hot it is, and some things about the elements that it consists of. Sound waves convey information to the listener, but also energy to the ear. This is true of all travelling waves; they convey energy and information along the direction of travel.

Variation of light intensity with distance from a point source

- You can consider the small lamp in Figure 16.3 to be a point source, radiating light uniformly in all directions.
- In a darkened room use a light meter to record measurements of light intensity at a range of distances from the lamp.
- Try to suggest a relationship between intensity and distance.

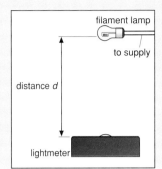

Figure 16.3   Measure the light
intensity at different distances

The inverse square law

You can observe from the above experiment that waves get weaker as they spread out from a source. At a greater distance from a source, the same power is spread over a larger area, so the power per unit area is less. The power per unit area is called the **energy flux** or **intensity**, and is defined as the energy that the wave carries perpendicularly through unit area each second. The unit of energy flux is watts per metres squared (W m⁻²). The symbol for energy flux is ϕ (the Greek letter *phi*, pronounced 'fy').

If waves spread out uniformly in all directions from a **point source**, there is a simple relationship between the flux and the distance from the source. Figure 16.4 shows a point source of waves. The power of the source (the energy it emits per second) is P. At a distance r from the source, this power is spread over a sphere of radius r and area $4\pi r^2$. So the energy flux ϕ is the power per unit area, in this case given by

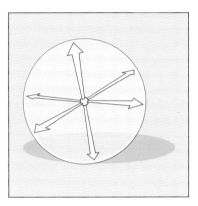

Figure 16.4   At a distance r, the light
spreads over area $4\pi r^2$

$$\text{energy flux} = \text{power/area} \quad \text{or} \quad \phi = P/4\pi r^2$$

This relationship is called the **inverse square law**. The energy flux will be reduced by a factor of 4 ($= 1/2^2$) when the distance is doubled, and reduced by a factor of 9 ($= 1/3^2$) when the distance is trebled.

Worked example

A mains lamp has a light output of 12 W. What is the energy flux (intensity) 2 m from the lamp? Assume that the lamp is a point source with its energy at any particular distance distributed over the surface of a sphere. For this example, the radius of the sphere is 2 m. The surface area of this sphere is

$$\text{surface area} = 4\pi r^2 = 4 \times \pi \times (2\text{ m})^2 = 50.3\text{ m}^2$$

and the energy flux is found from

$$\text{energy flux} = \frac{\text{power}}{\text{surface area}} = \frac{12\text{ W}}{50.3\text{ m}^2} = 0.24\text{ W m}^{-2}$$

Now find the rate at which light energy would be incident on this book if it were held open 2 m from and facing the lamp. What would be the effect of increasing this distance to 4 m?

Transverse and longitudinal waves

Waves down a spring

- Stretch a 'Slinky' spring along a desk top (Figure 17.1). Flick one end briefly along the line AB and back to send a single horizontal pulse along the spring. Move the end repeatedly along the same line to produce a continuous wave.

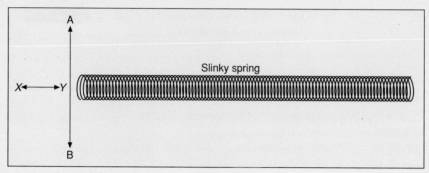

Figure 17.1 You can produce two types of wave on the spring

- Then gather together several coils at one end of the stretched 'Slinky' and suddenly release them to observe a different type of pulse moving along the spring. Move the end repeatedly in the direction XY to produce a continuous wave of the same type.
- Describe the difference between the two types of wave.

Transverse and longitudinal waves

You can produce two different types of waves down a 'Slinky' spring. In one type of wave, shown in Figure 17.2, the disturbances of the spring are perpendicular to the direction of travel of the wave. This type of wave is called a **transverse wave**.

If the disturbances of the spring are along the direction of oscillation, the wave is a **longitudinal wave**, as Figure 17.3 shows.

When you observe a candle in front of a loudspeaker, it shows that the oscillations associated with sound waves are parallel to the direction of travel. Sound waves are longitudinal.

It is easy to see the transverse components of water waves, because the surface of the water moves up and down as the wave spreads out. But the water also moves back and forwards as well; water waves are both longitudinal and transverse.

Electromagnetic waves such as radio waves, microwaves and light consist of electric and magnetic fields, which oscillate at right angles to each other and to their direction of travel. So electromagnetic waves are transverse.

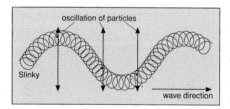

Figure 17.2 A transverse wave

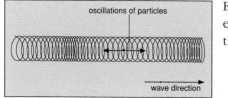

Figure 17.3 A longitudinal wave

Microwaves leaving a source

- Set up a microwave transmitter facing a receiver (Figure 17.4). Observe the strength of the received signal as you rotate the receiver through 360°.
- Repeat the experiment but leave the receiver stationary while rotating the transmitter.
- Align the receiver and transmitter for maximum signal. Place a grille of metal rods between them. What changes occur in the received intensity as the rods are rotated about the same horizontal axis?

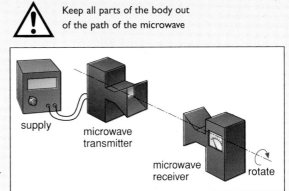

Keep all parts of the body out of the path of the microwave

Figure 17.4   *What happens when you rotate the receiver?*

Plane polarisation

Microwaves are transverse waves. Those leaving the transmitter consist of oscillations restricted to one direction, determined by the structure of the transmitter. Oscillations like this, where the direction of the oscillations and the direction of travel all lie in a single plane (Figure 17.5), are called **plane polarised**. Microwave receivers are polarised; they will only receive oscillations in one direction. If the polarisation of the receiver is the same as that of the transmitter, the signal received is strong. If the polarisation of the receiver is at right angles to that of the transmitter, no signal is received. A grille of metal rods acts as a filter, letting through signals of one polarisation, but reflecting back the other components.

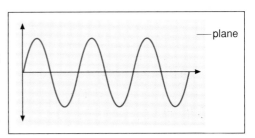

Figure 17.5   *The displacements and the direction of travel define a plane*

Polarising light

- Look at a lamp through a Polaroid filter.
- Then look through two Polaroid filters. Rotate one filter and observe what happens (Figure 17.6).
- Try to explain your observations.

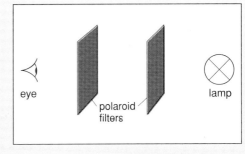

Figure 17.6   *Rotate one of the polaroids*

The light leaving a filament lamp is **unpolarised**; the oscillations are not confined to any single plane.

A Polaroid filter polarises the light, as it confines the oscillations to a single plane, as shown in Figure 17.7. A second Polaroid filter will stop the light if it is at right angles to the first filter. If it is at a different angle it will only let through a component of the polarised light from the first filter.

Both microwaves and visible light are transverse waves, and can therefore be polarised. In longitudinal waves, the oscillations are parallel to the direction of wave travel. It makes no sense, therefore, to think of confining them to a single plane. This explains why longitudinal waves, like sound, cannot be polarised.

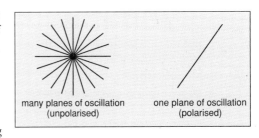

many planes of oscillation (unpolarised)

one plane of oscillation (polarised)

Figure 17.7   *End-on view of two beams of light*

Wave speed, wavelength and frequency

Measuring the speed of sound

- Watch a friend bang together two large flat pieces of wood some distance away across a sports field. Time the interval between seeing the impact and hearing the sound.
- Measure the distance that the sound has travelled and calculate its speed.
- What does this calculation assume?

Measuring the speed of light

- Use an oscilloscope to time how long it takes a flash of light to travel from a transmitter, to a distant mirror and back to a receiver, as shown in Figure 18.1.
- Then bring the mirror closer and measure the new time.
- Measure the change in travel distance of the light pulse and calculate the change in time. Use these to find the speed of light.
- Send the pulse through a length of fibre optic cable and calculate the speed of light through that.

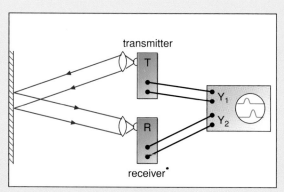

Figure 18.1   The oscilloscope times light pulses travelling from the transmitter to the receiver

A wide range of wave speeds

Sound waves travel typically at about $330 \, \text{m s}^{-1}$ in air. Some waves, for instance those on the surface of water, travel much more slowly. Light travels many times faster — about $300\,000\,000 \, \text{m s}^{-1}$ in air, and about two-thirds of that speed through an optical fibre.

The speed of most waves is not substantially affected by frequency. The different frequencies of sound contained in the music take about the same time to reach the back of a concert hall.

Investigating sound waves

- Set up the apparatus in Figure 18.2. Set the signal generator to give a sinusoidal output of 3 kHz. Check that the traces on the oscilloscope screen are similar when the microphones are side by side.
- Move the microphones apart, but keep them the same distance from the loudspeaker. What effect does this have on the traces on the oscilloscope's screen?
- Put the microphones together again and then move one of them further from the loudspeaker. Observe the effect. Identify two points in line with the loudspeaker that are one wavelength apart. Measure the wavelength.
- Repeat for different frequencies.

Figure 18.2   Compare the signals from the two microphones

Wavefronts

Imagine freezing a wave spreading out from a single source on a water surface. Figure 18.3 shows a slice of the snapshot. Along the dotted line P – P, a fixed distance from the source of waves, all the displacements of the water are in phase. Line P – P is a **wavefront** — a line joining points of the wave that are all in phase. The line Q – Q is another wavefront, some distance further from the source. As well as being in phase with each other, the points along the line Q – Q are also in phase with those along P – P. The wavefronts P – P and Q – Q are one wavelength apart. The minimum distance between two points on a wave that oscillate in phase is called the **wavelength**, λ. It is the distance from a point on one wavefront to the corresponding point on the next wavefront, as shown in Figure 18.4.

There is a simple connection between **wave speed**, frequency and wavelength. Since frequency = number of cycles each second, and wavelength = length of each cycle, we have that

frequency × wavelength = total length each second = speed of wave

$$f\lambda = c$$

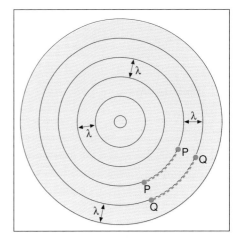

Figure 18.3   Wavefronts spread out from the source

Figure 18.4   Wavelength λ

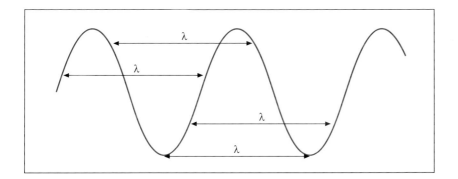

Worked example

Radio 5 broadcasts on the medium wave with a wavelength of 330 m. Taking the speed of radio waves as $3.0 \times 10^8 \, \text{m s}^{-1}$, calculate the frequency and the number of oscillations that the transmitter emits during a one hour programme.

Since $f\lambda = c$, we get

$$f = c/\lambda = (3 \times 10^8 \, \text{m s}^{-1})/(330 \, \text{m}) = 9.09 \times 10^5 \, \text{Hz} = 909 \, \text{kHz}$$

During one hour there are 3600 seconds. So in one hour there are

$$(9.09 \times 10^5 \, \text{oscillations/second}) \times 3600 \, \text{seconds} = 3.27 \times 10^9 \, \text{oscillations}$$

19 Diffraction and reflection

Making rays

- A ray box uses a lamp and a slit to make a narrow beam, or ray, of light. Figure 19.1 shows two metal barriers in a ripple tank. Try to use the apparatus to make a narrow ray of water ripples. Investigate the effect of changing the width of the gap in the barrier and changing the wavelength of the waves.
- In a darkened room, try to make a **laser** beam even narrower by passing it through a slit. Observe what happens when the slit gets very narrow.
- At a distance of 1 m from a microwave transmitter, measure the width of the beam. Then put two metal plates in front of the transmitter and measure the width again. Investigate the connection between gap width and beam width.

LASER BEAM

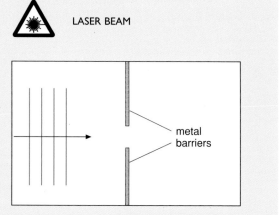

Figure 19.1   Send plane ripples towards a gap

Diffraction

Whenever waves pass through a small opening, they spread out. This is called **diffraction**. The amount of diffraction depends on the size of the aperture and on the wavelength of the waves. As Figure 19.2 shows, the narrower the opening, the greater the diffraction. Also, as Figure 19.3 shows, the larger the wavelength, the greater the diffraction. Diffraction is only noticeable when the size of the opening is comparable to the wavelength. With water waves, diffraction is noticeable with openings of a few centimetres. The wavelength of light is much smaller, and diffraction of light is only noticeable with very tiny openings.

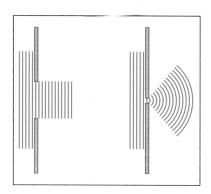

Figure 19.2   There is greater diffraction with a smaller gap

Rays and wavefronts

If you had a large ripple tank, you could make a series of flat wavefronts that would be a water **ray**. The wavefronts themselves are perpendicular to their own direction of travel; they are perpendicular to the rays.

A ray of light as well is a series of wavefronts as shown in Figure 19.4. All the light wavefronts are perpendicular to the light ray. Both rays and wavefronts are ways of considering the behaviour of waves.

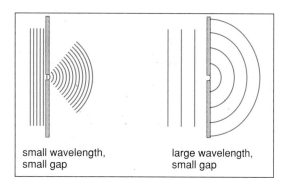

small wavelength, small gap

large wavelength, small gap

Figure 19.3   There is greater diffraction with larger wavelength

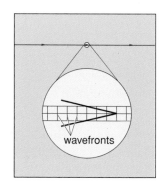

wavefronts

Figure 19.4   A ray is made of many wavefronts

Reflection

When waves travel through a uniform medium, their direction of travel remains the same. But if there is a change in the medium, or some form of obstruction, the waves may be reflected. **Reflection** literally means 'sent back'; waves that are reflected return to some extent in the direction from which they came. All waves can be reflected, but for obvious reasons reflection is easy to observe with light.

The laws of reflection

The following experiments show that:

> The angle of reflection is always equal to the angle of incidence.

> The incident ray, the reflected ray and the normal to the mirror at the point of incidence are all in the same plane.

The laws of reflection apply to all types of waves. Figure 19.5 shows some examples of reflection of water waves.

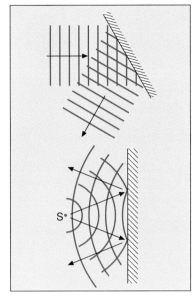

Figure 19.5   Reflection of water waves

Reflection of light

- In a darkened room, use a ray box to direct a ray of light at a mirror, as shown in Figure 19.6. Observe the reflected ray.
- The ray hitting the mirror is called the incident ray; the ray bouncing back is the reflected ray. Measure the angle of incidence and the angle of reflection relative to the normal (perpendicular) to the mirror's surface at the point of incidence. Repeat the measurements for a range of incident angles.
- Shine a laser onto a mirror. Shake a dusty cloth nearby to show the path of the beam. Fix rulers along the incident ray, the reflected ray and the normal to the surface. What do you observe?

LASER BEAM

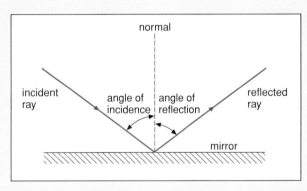

Figure 19.6   Measure the angle of incidence and the angle of reflection

Reflection of microwaves

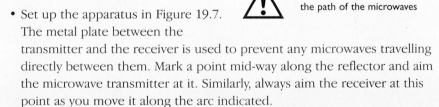

Keep all body parts out of the path of the microwaves

- Set up the apparatus in Figure 19.7. The metal plate between the transmitter and the receiver is used to prevent any microwaves travelling directly between them. Mark a point mid-way along the reflector and aim the microwave transmitter at it. Similarly, always aim the receiver at this point as you move it along the arc indicated.
- Adjust the position of the receiver until it detects the maximum signal. The angles of incidence and reflection should then be measured.
- Repeat for a range of incident angles.

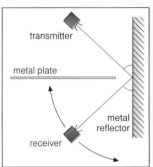

Figure 19.7   Investigating microwave reflection

Waves in deep and shallow water

- Use a rectangular sheet of glass to create a shallow area a few millimetres deep in part of a ripple tank. Send plane waves perpendicularly towards the edge of the plate. What happens to the speed, wavelength and frequency of the ripples as they go from deep to shallow water?
- Measure the wave speed in both deep and shallow water.
- Repeat the above experiment but turn the glass plate so that the water waves approach it at an angle, as shown in Figure 20.1. Sketch the pattern of the wavefronts either side of the boundary between the deep and shallow water.
- Measure, as accurately as possible, the angles at which the waves approach and then travel across the glass plate.

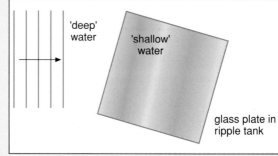

Figure 20.1   Wave approaching an angled boundary

Changing wave speed

When a wave crosses into shallower water, it slows down. The wavefronts in the deep water behind are travelling faster. They catch up with slower waves in front and get closer. So both the wavelength and the speed are reduced in the shallow water.

In the shallow water, the waves are slower and closer together. In the deep water, the waves are faster but further apart. In both the deep and shallow water, the number of waves that pass a point in each second — the frequency — remains the same.

If the speed and wavelength in the deep water are c_1 and λ_1, and the speed and wavelength in the shallow water are c_2 and λ_2, then the frequency is given by the following:

$$f = c_1/\lambda_1 = c_2/\lambda_2 \qquad \text{so that} \qquad c_1/c_2 = \lambda_1/\lambda_2$$

Refraction

If a plane water wave strikes a boundary between deep and shallow water at an angle, each part of a wavefront reaches shallower water at a different time. The parts in the shallower water slow down and get left slightly behind by the parts still moving in the deep water. So the wavefront changes its direction of travel, as shown in Figure 20.2. This change in direction at the boundary where the wave speed changes is called **refraction**.

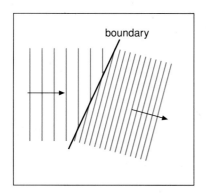

Figure 20.2   Wavefront refraction at a boundary

Refraction of light

- Use a ray box to send a ray of light into one side of a glass block. Observe the path taken by the ray of light as it passes into and through the glass block.
- Mark the position of the block and the path of the light on the paper. Remove the block and measure the angle in air, θ_1, and the angle in the glass, θ_2 (Figure 20.3).
- Repeat for a range of incident angles. Try to find a relationship between θ_1 and θ_2.
- Replace the glass block with a rectangular, thin-sided plastic tank containing water. Repeat your previous measurements. Again, try to find a relationship between the angles you measure.

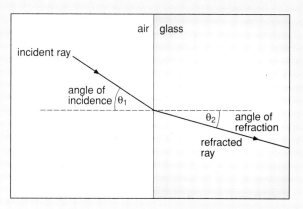

Figure 20.3   Measure the angles in the air and in the glass

Snell's law

Figure 20.4 shows some wavefronts travelling from medium 1 to medium 2, in which they travel more slowly. The wavelength changes from λ_1 to λ_2 as the wave goes from medium 1 to medium 2. Angles θ_1 and θ_2 (θ is the Greek letter *theta*) are the angles between the waves and the normal in the two media. You can also see that they are the angles between the wavefronts in the two media and the surface.

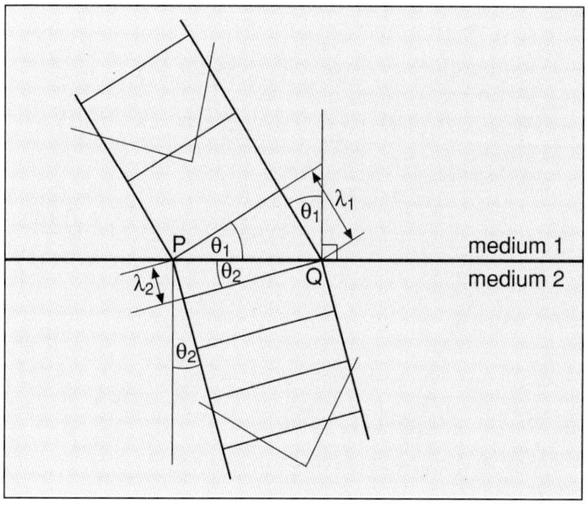

From the geometry of the diagram:

$$\sin \theta_1 = \lambda_1/PQ \qquad \text{and} \qquad \sin \theta_2 = \lambda_2/PQ$$

from which we get

Figure 20.4   Refraction diagram

$$PQ = \lambda_1/\sin \theta_1 = \lambda_2/\sin \theta_2 \qquad \text{so} \qquad \sin \theta_1/\sin \theta_2 = \lambda_1/\lambda_2$$

From the equation on page 46 $c_1/c_2 = \lambda_1/\lambda_2$ we have

$$\sin \theta_1/\sin \theta_2 = c_1/c_2$$

The values of c_1 and c_2 are constants for the two media. So their ratio is also a constant. Therefore, when a ray goes from one medium to another, the ratio of the sines of the angles in the two media is a constant for those two media. This is known as **Snell's law**.

You know from Chapter 18 that the speeds of light in an optical fibre and in air are respectively $2 \times 10^8\,\text{m s}^{-1}$ and $3 \times 10^8\,\text{m s}^{-1}$. So for light travelling from air to glass:

$$\sin \theta_1/\sin \theta_2 = c_1/c_2 = (3 \times 10^8\,\text{m s}^{-1})/(2 \times 10^8\,\text{m s}^{-1}) = 1.5$$

Refractive index

The theory of refraction was important even before the speed of light in any medium was known. Opticians were unable to calculate speeds themselves, and so based their calculations on the ratio of speeds in different media, called the **refractive index**. The refractive index, n, of a medium is the ratio of the speed at which light moves in vacuum to the speed at which it moves in the medium.

For two different media

$$n_1 = c/c_1 \quad \text{and} \quad n_2 = c/c_2$$

$$c = c_1 n_1 = c_2 n_2 \quad \text{so} \quad c_1/c_2 = n_2/n_1$$

Using the equation $\sin\theta_1/\sin\theta_2 = c_1/c_2$ from Chapter 20, this gives:

$$\sin\theta_1/\sin\theta_2 = c_1/c_2 = n_2/n_1$$

and so

$$n_1\sin\theta_1 = n_2\sin\theta_2$$

Another way to put this is to say that

$$n\sin\theta = \text{constant}$$

Table 21.1 lists some values of refractive indices.

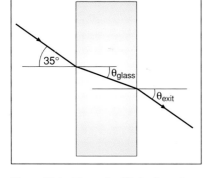

Figure 21.1   The path of light through a glass block

Table 21.1   *Refractive index values*

Material	Refractive index
vacuum	1.0
air	1.0
water	1.3
glass	1.5
diamond	2.4

Using refractive index

Figure 21.1 shows a beam of light entering one side of a parallel glass block at an angle of 35° to the normal. What are the other angles marked?

The speed of light in air is almost the same as the speed of light in a vacuum. So the refractive index of air is 1.0. The refractive index of glass is 1.5.

We use the equation $n\sin\theta = \text{constant}$, which is true throughout the path of the ray because the sides of the block are parallel. So we get

$$n_{air}\sin\theta_{air} = 1 \times \sin 35° = 0.574$$

$$n_{glass}\sin\theta_{glass} = 1.5 \times \sin\theta_{glass} = 0.574$$

$$\sin\theta_{glass} = 0.574/1.5 \quad \text{so} \quad \theta_{glass} = 22.5°$$

So the angle in the glass at the first face between the ray and the normal is 22.5°. Since the sides of the block are parallel, this is the angle between the ray and the normal at the second face. When the beam of light emerges from the far side of the block, it is once again travelling through a medium with a refractive index of 1.0. The angle that it makes with the normal to the boundary returns to 35°. The beam now moves parallel to its original direction, although it has been displaced from it.

Light through a prism

- What happens to the beam of white light as it passes into, through and out the other side of the prism in Figure 21.2? Sketch the prism and the paths taken.
- Which colour is refracted the most? How does the speed of blue light in glass compare with that of red light?
- Measure the angle between the emerging blue light and the direction of the incident white light.
- Repeat for the emerging red light.

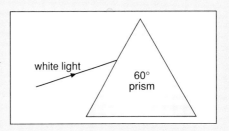

Figure 21.2   Shine a beam of white light at the prism

Deviation

Figure 21.3 shows a ray of light of a single frequency (a **monochromatic** ray, literally 'single colour') passing through a prism. The prism deviates the ray from its original direction. The **angle of deviation** is the angle between the original and the final beam directions.

Dispersion

The frequency of blue light is higher than that of red light, and the speed in glass varies with the frequency of the light. In air, the speeds of red and blue light are the same; but in glass, blue light is slower than red light. So the refractive index of blue light is greater than that of red light.

Figure 21.4 shows white light passing through a prism. The different colours in the white light are deviated by different amounts. Blue light has been refracted more than red light. The angle of deviation is greater for blue light than it is for red light. This is called **dispersion**.

The colours that make up white light follow sufficiently different paths to become distinct, and a spectrum is observed. The prism splits the white light up into a range of frequencies. We have seven different names for different sections of the spectrum — but really there are no distinct boundaries.

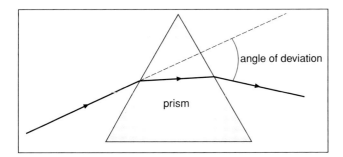

Figure 21.3   The prism deviates the monochromatic ray

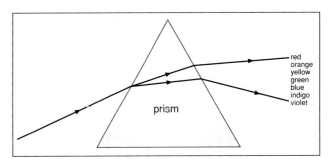

Figure 21.4   White light is dispersed as well as deviated

Total internal reflection

Rays leaving glass

- Direct a narrow ray of light onto the curved side of the block. Aim the ray directly at the mid-point of the straight side of the block (Figure 22.1). The ray will enter the block normally (ie at right angles to the curve) and travel along a radius without any deviation.
- Starting with a small angle of incidence within the block (10°), measure the angle of refraction as the ray leaves the block. Repeat for incident angles of 20°, 30° and 40°.
- Use your measurements to find the ratio of the speed of light in glass to that in air.
- What happens when you increase the angle of incidence to 50° and beyond? Measure the angle of incidence that produces an angle of refraction of 90°.

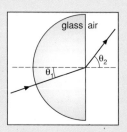

Figure 22.1 Light through a semicircular glass block

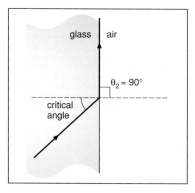

Figure 22.2   Light just emerging from glass

Critical angle

A ray bends away from the normal when it goes from glass to air. But, as Figure 22.2 shows, the ray only just emerges from the glass when the angle of incidence is around 40°. If the ray strikes the glass at a greater angle, refraction is impossible, and the ray is **totally internally reflected**. The **critical angle** is the maximum angle of incidence for refraction to occur.

Below the critical angle (Figure 22.3a), light is partially refracted through the boundary and partially reflected from it. Above the critical angle (Figure 22.3b), all the light energy is reflected from the boundary as though it were a perfect mirror.

You can calculate the critical angle for two media from the refractive index or from the speeds of the waves in the two media. Since $n \sin \theta =$ constant

$$n_{glass} \times \sin(\text{critical angle}) = n_{air} \times \sin 90°$$

Since $n_{air} = 1.0$, $\sin 90° = 1.0$ and $n_{air}/n_{glass} = c_{glass}/c_{air}$, we obtain

$$\sin(\text{critical angle}) = 1/n_{glass} = c_{glass}/c_{air}$$

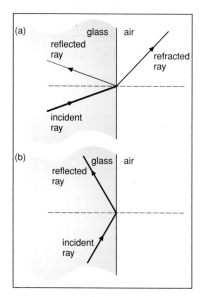

Figure 22.3   Rays striking a boundary (a) below and (b) above the critical angle

Applications of total internal reflection

- Aim a ray of light normally at one of the short sides of a right-angled isosceles prism. Why is the angle of deviation 90°?
- Aim the ray normally at the long side. Why is the angle of deviation now 180°?
- Observe one end of a glass rod when its other end is held close to a light source. Notice how the light is trapped within and travels along the glass rod. Use a glass fibre to show that the light still travels along even a twisted path.

Totally reflecting prisms

The critical angle for a glass – air boundary is typically about 42°. A right-angled isosceles prism can reverse the direction of a ray of light. The light enters the longest side normally and strikes one of the sloping sides at an angle of 45°. Since this exceeds the critical angle, the light is totally internally reflected at an angle of 45°. It then strikes the other sloping side at 45°, again undergoing total internal reflection. The ray is now moving parallel to its initial direction, but in the opposite direction.

Figure 22.4 shows two such prisms used to reduce the length of a pair of binoculars while still maintaining the long light path required for large magnification. One advantage of using prisms rather than mirrors is that all the light is reflected – the reflection is total.

Optical fibre systems

Some of the telephone calls that you make will be, at some point along their journey, turned into coded pulses of laser light. These are then sent along **optical fibres** by a series of total internal reflections (Figure 22.5).

Step-index fibres contain a central core with a slightly larger refractive index than the surrounding cladding. There are two types: **multimode** and **monomode**. The graphs in Figure 22.6 show how the refractive index changes across each type of fibre.

The wider core of a multimode cable allows light to enter the fibre at different angles (modes) and follow different length paths through it. Light takes more time to travel the longer paths, and a short, sharp pulse entering the fibre may be spread out (or dispersed) by the time that it reaches the other end of the cable. The much narrower core of the monomode fibre overcomes this problem by restricting the light to virtually a single path (one mode). Monomode fibres are harder to make and therefore more expensive.

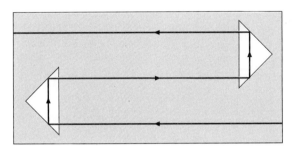

Figure 22.4   Use of right-angled prisms in binoculars

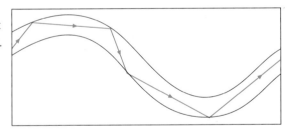

Figure 22.5   Light path within a glass fibre

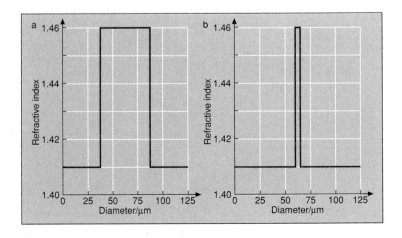

Figure 22.6   Refractive index profile for (a) multimode and (b) monomode fibres

The principle of superposition

Waves on springs

- Stretch a long 'Slinky' spring between yourself and a friend. Simultaneously send a single pulse from each end along the spring.
- What happens when the pulses meet? Do they pass through or reflect off each other? You may need to send two very different pulses to answer the last question.
- Experiment with pulses of different shapes, including some with opposite displacements. Pay particular attention to the shape and size of the combined pulse when the two pulses meet.

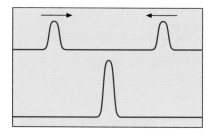

Figure 23.1 The pulses add up where they cross

Superposition

When two pulses travelling in opposite directions on a spring meet, they pass straight through each other. As Figure 23.1 shows, while they are crossing, the combined pulse is the addition of the two separate pulses.

The displacements of the pulses are vector quantities. Their resultant takes into account their direction. If the pulses have the same direction, they add up to give a larger resultant displacement. If the pulses have opposite directions, they totally or partially cancel out.

This same effect is evident with continuous waves. When two waves of the same type cross, the displacement at any point is equal to the vector sum of the displacements of each of the waves at that point. This is called the **principle of superposition**. (Superposition means 'placing on top'.)

Superposition of water waves

- Use the arrangement in Figure 23.2 to make two regular sets of overlapping circular waves. Observe the pattern produced. Where are the waves large? Where are the waves small?
- Now use the arrangement in Figure 23.3 to make two sets of circular ripples from plane ripples. Observe the superposition effects and compare them with those produced by waves from the two dippers.

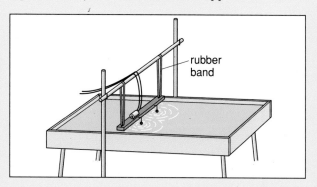

Figure 23.2 Superposition occurs where the waves cross

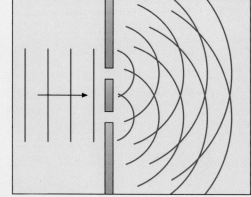

Figure 23.3 You can use two gaps to make two sets of waves

Superposition patterns

You can produce sets of circular waves either with separate dippers or using diffraction through holes in a barrier. However you do it, the two overlapping sets of circular water waves produce a complicated pattern like that in Figure 23.4. In some places the directions of the varying wave displacements from the two sources are the same. The waves are in phase, so they reinforce each other. This is **constructive superposition** (sometimes called constructive interference). In other places the directions of the varying wave displacements from the two sources are opposite. The waves are out of phase, so they cancel. This is **destructive superposition** (or destructive interference).

Where the waves arriving at a point are in phase, there is constructive superposition. When the waves are in antiphase (π out of phase), there is destructive superposition.

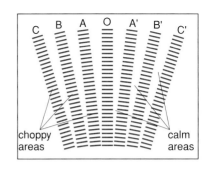

Figure 23.4   A superposition pattern on water shows calm areas and choppy ones

Using separate sources

- Use the two separate vibrator and dipper assemblies to make two sets of circular waves (Figure 23.5). Try to set both dippers vibrating at the same frequency. Observe the resulting superposition pattern.
- With the vibrating frequencies the same, start and stop one vibrator. Observe what happens to the pattern.
- What happens to the pattern if the frequencies are different?

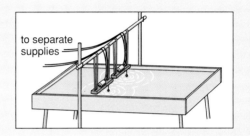

Figure 23.5   These dippers vibrate independently

Coherence

Two sources of different frequencies will not produce a stable superposition pattern. Places where the waves are in phase at one instant will become out of phase the next. If the two sources have very close frequencies, you may be able to see a pattern that moves slowly. If the frequencies are very different, the pattern will move so quickly that it will be impossible to see.

For superposition patterns to be stable and observable, the waves that produce them must be of the same frequency.

If the sources producing a superposition pattern have the same frequency, but are out of phase with each other, a stable pattern will be produced. But if one or both keeps starting and stopping, so that they are sometimes in phase with each other and sometimes out of phase, then the pattern will not be stable.

For a stable superposition pattern, the sources of waves must be **coherent**. This means that they must have the same frequency, and any phase difference must be constant.

The effect of amplitude on superposition

If two sources of waves have very different amplitudes, then you will not observe superposition patterns. The wave with the larger amplitude will dominate, because it makes little difference to the total whether the wave with the smaller amplitude is in phase or out of phase with it. When the waves have similar amplitude, cancellation is noticeable. And if the amplitudes are identical, then cancellation can be complete.

Two source superposition experiments

Superposition of sound waves

- Set up the apparatus of Figure 24.1 on a large sheet of paper. The two loudspeakers connected to the single signal generator produce two coherent sets of sound waves.
- Adjust the output of the signal generator to 3 kHz. Locate positions of maximum and minimum sound intensity.
- Check that there is constructive superposition along a line equidistant from both speakers.
- Locate and mark the other lines of constructive superposition and the lines of destructive superposition.

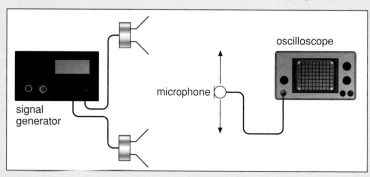

Figure 24.1   Detecting a sound superposition pattern

Path difference and phase difference

Figure 24.2 shows the superposition pattern produced by two loudspeakers vibrating in phase. It is the same as the pattern produced by two sources of water waves.

Along the central line O there is constructive superposition. Waves from S_1 and S_2 travel the same distance (the same path length) to any point on the line. So the waves are in phase along that line. There is no phase difference and hence there is constructive superposition. This central line is called the **central maximum**.

At any point along the curved line A, the path length of the wave from S_1 is a whole wavelength longer than the path length of the wave from S_2. The **path difference** is a whole wavelength; the waves arriving on the line are 2π out of phase, which is like being in phase, so there is still constructive superposition. Midway between lines O and A there is a region of destructive superposition where the path difference is half a wavelength and the phase difference is π.

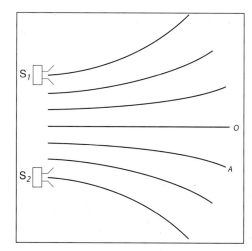

Figure 24.2   The lines show the regions of constructive superposition

Superposition with microwaves

- Set up the apparatus in Figure 24.3. Diffraction at the two gaps in the metal plates produces two coherent sets of microwaves from the single transmitter. The amplifier and loudspeaker indicate the strength of the microwaves received by the probe.
- Mark the position of each slit on the paper. Move the detector along the line shown. Mark and label the positions of maximum and of minimum signal strength on the sheet of paper.
- Measure the distance from the centre of each slit to the points of maximum and minimum signal strength. Use these distances to find an average value for the wavelength of the microwaves.

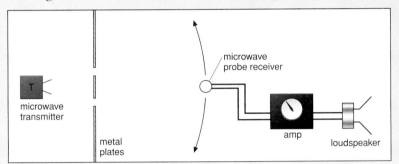

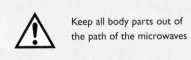

Keep all body parts out of the path of the microwaves

Figure 24.3   Superposition of microwaves

Path difference

Figure 24.4 shows two sources of microwaves at S_1 and S_2. The microwaves leave the two slits S_1 and S_2 in phase. The point O is the same distance from both slits. The path difference is zero. The waves are in phase when they reach O and so there is constructive superposition. O is on the central maximum.

The distance from S_2 to A is greater than the distance from S_1 to A by an amount λ. So the waves arriving at point A are in phase. There is constructive superposition. Midway between O and A, the path difference is λ/2. The waves are out of phase, so there is destructive superposition. At point B, the path difference is 2λ; there is constructive superposition. Midway between A and B, the path difference is $1\frac{1}{2}λ$, and there is destructive superposition.

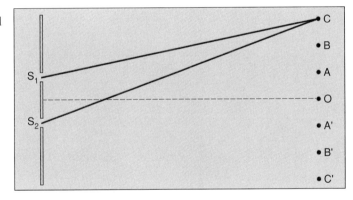

Figure 24.4   A maximum occurs at C when $S_2C - S_1C = 3λ$

In general:

> For constructive superposition, path difference = $nλ$.

> For destructive superposition, path difference = $(n + \frac{1}{2})λ$.

The series of maxima and minima are known as fringes.

25 Superposition of light

Producing coherent light sources

Light sources, even monochromatic ones, produce bursts of waves with different phase relationships, rather than a continuous coherent wave. The light from a filament lamp is particularly incoherent, as each part of the filament produces its own set of incoherent waves.

A small slit in front of a filament lamp samples only a fraction of the light from the filament and diffracts it. That diffracted light is coherent with itself at least. With a filter to make it monochromatic, the light can be used to demonstrate superposition, as shown in Figure 25.1.

Light from a laser is already monochromatic and much more coherent. It is also much brighter. It is much easier to demonstrate superposition of light with a laser.

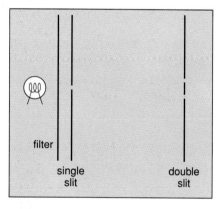

Figure 25.1   Producing two sources of coherent light

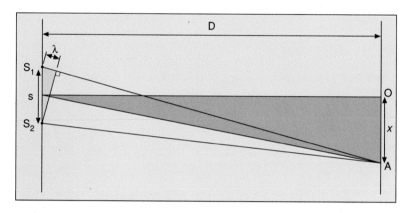

Figure 25.2   The two shaded triangles are similar, so $\lambda/s = x/D$

The double source equation

Figure 25.2 shows two wave sources, S_1 and S_2, a distance s apart. They produce a central maximum at O, and the first maximum next to that (the first **subsidiary maximum**) a distance x away at point A. If distance D is large, then the two shaded triangles are similar. So

$$\lambda/s = x/D \qquad \text{so} \qquad \lambda = xs/D$$

You can use this formula to measure the wavelength of light. The distance x is the fringe width. Not only is it the spacing between the central maximum and the first maximum at one side, it is also the spacing between any two adjacent fringes near the centre of the superposition pattern.

Young's double slit experiment

- Use a laser to illuminate two narrow slits about 0.5 mm apart. Light diffracts at the slits and the two overlapping sets of waves produce a superposition pattern on the screen (Figure 25.3).
- Measure the width of several fringes and calculate x, the fringe width.
- Measure also the slit separation and the distance between the screen and the slits. Use these, and the formula $\lambda = xs/D$, to calculate the wavelength of the laser light.

LASER BEAM

Figure 25.3   Typical arrangement when using a laser

Monochromatic and chromatic fringes

Figure 25.4 shows the superposition pattern produced by red laser light. The slit spacing was 0.14 mm and the slit – screen distance 3.0 m. You can use the scale marked on the photograph to calculate the wavelength of the light. Each division represents 1 cm.

The wavelength of violet light is about 4×10^{-7} m (400 nm) while that of red light is about 7×10^{-7} m (700 nm). So red light gives a larger fringe spacing than blue light when both are used in the same double slit experiment. If slits are illuminated by both red and blue light simultaneously, the red fringes start getting mixed up with the blue fringes.

Figure 25.5 shows the fringe pattern produced by white light. You can see that the first subsidiary blue maximum is close to the central maximum, and the first subsidiary red maximum is further from the central maximum. This produces a blue tinge to one edge of the first subsidiary maximum and a red tinge to the other edge. Notice how the fringes become less distinct the further out they are from the central maximum, as the differently coloured fringes overlap more.

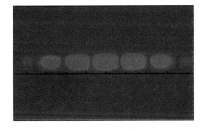

Figure 25.4   Superposition pattern for laser light through a double slit

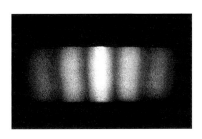

Figure 25.5   Superposition pattern caused by white light through a double slit

Worked example

A yellow lamp produces a wavelength of 550 nm. Light from this lamp passes through a single slit and illuminates a double slit, which has a slit separation of 0.45 mm. A screen is placed 2.1 m away from the double slit. Calculate the fringe width.

Since

$$\text{wavelength} = \frac{\text{fringe spacing} \times \text{slit separation}}{\text{distance to screen}}$$

we have

$$\text{fringe spacing} = \frac{\text{wavelength} \times \text{distance to screen}}{\text{slit separation}}$$

so

$$\text{fringe spacing} = [(550 \times 10^{-9} \text{m}) \times 2.1\,\text{m}]/(0.45 \times 10^{-3}\text{m})$$

$$= 2.6 \times 10^{-3}\text{m} = 2.6\,\text{mm}$$

Stationary waves

More waves on springs

- Stretch a long 'Slinky' spring between yourself and a friend. Simultaneously send waves of the same frequency from both ends. Observe what happens as the waves cross.
- Adjust the frequency to produce a regular pattern of oscillation. Sketch this pattern. Try to produce other patterns.
- Fix one end of the spring firmly and send waves from the free end. What happens to these waves when they reach the far end of the spring? Again, try to produce a range of patterns.

Waves in opposite directions

There are two ways of investigating the effect of identical waves travelling in opposite directions on a spring. Either you can produce the waves directly, sending them from opposite directions down a spring, or you can send one wave down and observe it crossing its own returning reflection.

When identical travelling waves cross in this way, they produce a wave shape that stands still on the spring, called a **stationary wave**.

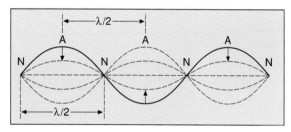

Figure 26.1   A stationary wave

Nodes and antinodes

Figure 26.1 shows a stationary wave on a spring. Some points on the spring, labelled N, always remain stationary. The amplitude of oscillation is zero. These places are called **nodes**. At other places, labelled A, the spring vibrates with maximum amplitude. These places are called **antinodes**. Adjacent nodes, or adjacent antinodes, are half a wavelength apart.

Stationary microwaves

- Direct a microwave transmitter at an aluminium plate reflector. Move a probe receiver along the line between the transmitter and the plate, and observe the nodes and antinodes (Figure 26.2).
- Measure the average distance between several adjacent nodes, and use this to calculate the wavelength of the microwaves.

 Keep all body parts out of the path of the microwaves

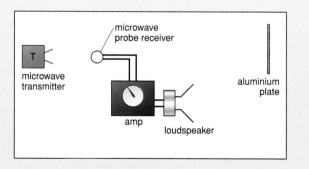

Figure 26.2   The forward and reflected microwaves produce a stationary wave

Constructive and destructive superposition

Nodes are places of no displacement. Nodes occur when the varying displacements of the two waves arriving at a point from opposite directions always cancel out. The wave displacements are equal and opposite to each other at all times. When the wave that is moving to the right through a node is at its positive maximum, the wave moving to the left is at its negative maximum. Destructive superposition occurs. Any displacement of one of the waves is cancelled out by an equal and opposite displacement of the other wave.

Antinodes are places of maximum amplitude. They occur when the two waves arriving at a point are in phase. Constructive superposition takes place, and the amplitude is twice that of each individual wave.

Energy and standing waves

A travelling wave conveys energy in the direction of travel. A stationary wave consists of two identical travelling waves going in opposite directions. You might imagine that this conveys equal energies in opposite directions. The net effect of this is that there is no energy transfer. A stationary wave conveys no energy at all.

Waves on a tensioned rubber cord

- Tension a rubber cord and anchor the ends. Use a signal generator to set the cord vibrating at a frequency of 1 Hz (Figure 26.3). Gradually increase the frequency until there is a stationary wave pattern. Sketch this pattern. Measure the wavelength and record its frequency.
- Continue to increase the frequency slowly until the next stationary wave pattern is produced. Again, sketch this and record its frequency and wavelength.
- Repeat this procedure for the first five stationary wave patterns. How do the frequencies of the different patterns compare?
- Use your results to find the speed of waves on the rubber cord.

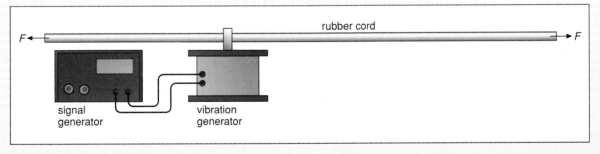

Figure 26.3   Producing stationary waves on a rubber cord

Oscillations of a stationary wave

The first, or fundamental, mode of oscillation of the standing wave on the rubber cord occurs at the **fundamental frequency** f. As Figure 26.4 shows, at this frequency the wavelength is twice the length of the cord. The cord has a node at each end, with a single antinode in the middle.

STATIONARY WAVES

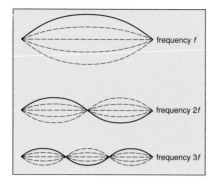

frequency f

frequency 2f

frequency 3f

Figure 26.4   Different modes of vibration

The next stationary wave pattern is observed at *2f*, twice the fundamental frequency. The wavelength is half as much, and twice as many node-to-node loops can fit onto the cord. You can get further stationary wave patterns at integer multiples of the fundamental frequency. These are the **harmonic frequencies** (*2f, 3f, 4f*, etc).

A larger frequency is required to produce each pattern if the tension in the rubber cord is increased. The wavelength remains fixed (length of cord constant), indicating an increase in the wave speed with tension.

Phase along a standing wave

All particles in a medium between two adjacent nodes move in the same direction together; they vibrate in phase with each other. Particles either side of a node move in opposite directions; they are vibrating out of phase with each other.

Stationary sound waves

- Point a loudspeaker at a hard wall. Set the signal generator to give a frequency of about 3 kHz. Use the microphone and oscilloscope to locate the nodes and antinodes (Figure 26.5). Measure the frequency and the wavelength.
- Change the frequency to obtain a different stationary wave pattern. Record a series of corresponding readings of frequency and wavelength.
- Plot a graph of frequency against 1/wavelength. Use the gradient of this graph to find the speed of sound in air.

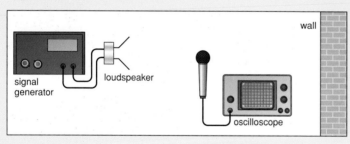

wall

signal generator

loudspeaker

oscilloscope

Figure 26.5   Producing stationary sound waves

Music and stationary waves

Figure 26.6   Stationary waves produce most orchestral sounds

Most musical instruments use stationary waves to produce their notes (Figure 26.6). Stringed instruments use the transverse stationary waves on a string. You hear the fundamental frequency of oscillation of the string, but the presence and relative strengths of harmonic frequencies present gives each musical instrument its own characteristic sound. Wind instruments rely on the production of longitudinal stationary waves in columns of vibrating air.

Quantum physics

An exciting place to be, particularly for atoms!

Photoelectric emission

The discharging electroscope

- An electroscope has a thin gold leaf attached to a metal stem. When the electroscope is charged, the leaf stands out.
- Use an EHT power supply of 5mA or less to charge an electroscope negatively (Figure 27.1). Disconnect the power supply and watch the electroscope for a minute. Does it discharge?
- Repeat the experiment, but this time shine ultra-violet radiation on to the electroscope. Is there a difference?
- Repeat the experiment yet again, but this time put a clean strip of zinc on the top cap (Figure 27.2).
- Experiment with a positively charged electroscope, with strong visible light, and with dull, oxidised zinc.

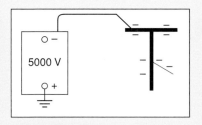

Figure 27.1   Charging an electroscope

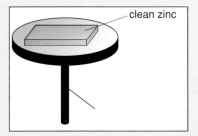

Figure 27.2   Put a cleaned strip of zinc on the electroscope

ULTRA-VIOLET RADIATION

NON-IONISING RADIATION

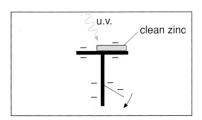

Figure 27.3   The leaf goes down

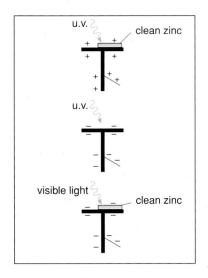

Figure 27.4   The leaf stays up

Photoelectric emission

When you connect the negative terminal of a power supply to an electroscope, some electrons transfer to the electroscope, making it negative too. The leaf on the electroscope then has the same sign of charge as the stem, so the two repel each other and the leaf stands out. The insulation on an electroscope is usually good, so very little charge leaks away and the leaf stays out. But, in certain circumstances, when you illuminate the top cap with the correct kind of radiation, an electroscope with a good insulator can still discharge rapidly.

In the situation shown in Figure 27.3, the leaf goes down, even with nothing touching the electroscope. The leaf discharges only if the zinc is shiny, if the illumination is ultra-violet and if the charge is negative. It does not discharge if the zinc is dull or if there is no zinc, with just bright light, or with positive charge (Figure 27.4).

You might at first think that the ultra-violet light is causing the air around the electroscope to conduct electricity, and so discharge the electroscope. But if so, the electroscope would also discharge if it were charged positively. If ionisation of air were the explanation, why should a zinc plate be necessary? Perhaps the ultra-violet light might be giving positive charge to the electroscope to neutralise it. But if so, why is there discharge when the zinc plate is on the top cap, but no discharge with a chromium top alone?

A likely explanation for the discharge is that ultra-violet radiation is causing the zinc to emit electrons and make itself less negative. This emission is **photoelectric emission** (literally 'emission of electrons by light').

usually from a metal surface.

Threshold frequency

Photoelectric emission from zinc only occurs if the radiation illuminating the zinc has a frequency of 1×10^{15} Hz or higher. This is in the ultra-violet region, just outside the visible spectrum. This frequency is called the **threshold frequency** for zinc.

Weak radiation above the threshold frequency will cause photoelectric emission, but radiation below the threshold frequency will not cause photoelectric emission, even if it is powerful. This observation puzzled physicists for some years.

Photons

In 1905, Einstein suggested an explanation for photoelectric emission based on a theory proposed by Planck. He suggested that electromagnetic radiation – visible light, ultra-violet light, or any other frequency — comes in small packets of energy, rather than in a steady stream. The general name for a small packet of energy is a **quantum**, but a packet, or quantum, of electromagnetic radiation is called a **photon**. The energy of a photon does not depend on the intensity of the radiation, but rather on its frequency.

When the frequency of the radiation is low, the energy of the photons is small; when the frequency is high, the energy of the photons is large.

The electrons in the metal are being bombarded with a stream of photons. An electron is only emitted if it interacts with a photon that has sufficient energy, on its own, to detach the electron from the metal. When photons of lower energy hit the metal, no electrons are emitted.

Work function

There is no photoelectric emission from zinc unless it is illuminated with radiation of frequency greater than its threshold frequency of about 1×10^{15} Hz. If you investigate other substances, you find that they each have a different threshold frequency.

Generally, the threshold frequencies are lower for substances that are chemically more reactive. These substances lose electrons more easily both in chemical reactions and photoelectrically. The lower threshold frequency corresponds to photons of lower energy; it means that you do not need photons of such high energy to release electrons from more reactive substances.

The minimum energy needed to remove electrons from a substance is called the **work function**, symbol ϕ (the Greek letter *phi*). The work function for zinc is less than the work function for chromium, which is why the threshold frequency for zinc is lower than the threshold frequency for chromium. This explains why radiation that causes photoelectric emission from the zinc plate does not necessarily cause emission from the chromium cap.

Einstein's photoelectric equation

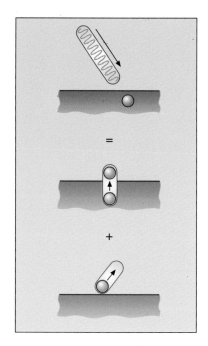

Figure 28.1   Photon energy = work function + electron kinetic energy

The energy of photoelectrons

When a photon ejects an electron, some of the photon's energy is used to free the electron from the material, and the rest gives kinetic energy to the electron (Figure 28.1). The easiest electrons to eject are those near the surface of the material, which need only the work function to release them. So more of the energy of the photons can be transferred to these electrons as kinetic energy. For these, the fastest electrons, the photon energy is equal to the work function plus the electron kinetic energy.

Other electrons need more energy than the work function to eject them. When a photon ejects these electrons, they have less kinetic energy than the fastest electrons. So with a given substance and given frequency of illumination, photoelectrons are emitted with a range of kinetic energies. But these energies have a clear maximum, which is the energy of the electrons that are easiest to remove from the metal. So if you measure the kinetic energy of the fastest emitted electrons, you can find out about both the photon energy and the work function of the metal.

To measure the energy of the electrons, you provide an electrical hill for them to run up. It is rather like measuring the energy of a bullet by finding how high it will rise when you shoot it upwards.

Measuring the energy of a photoelectron

- The photoelectric cell in Figure 28.2 has two electrodes. Light illuminates the large emitting electrode, which has a low work function. Photons with sufficient energy cause photoelectric emission. If any photoelectrons reach the receiving electrode, the picoammeter indicates a current.
- The battery and potentiometer make the receiving electrode in the photoelectric cell negative. This provides an electrical hill that photoelectrons must run up. The trick is to increase the repelling voltage slowly from zero until the current drops to zero. At this voltage, called the stopping voltage (or stopping potential), the electrical hill is just high enough to stop even the fastest electrons arriving.
- At the stopping voltage, the kinetic energy lost by the fastest electrons is equal to the electrical potential energy they gain going up the hill.
- Shine lights of different known frequencies onto the emitting electrode. For each frequency, measure the stopping voltage.
- Plot a graph of stopping voltage against frequency. What is the relation between them?

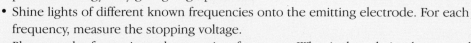

Figure 28.2   The electrons are repelled back to the emitting electrode

ULTRA-VIOLET RADIATION

Calculating photon energy

Einstein accepted Planck's hypothesis that the energy of each photon is proportional to its frequency:

$$E \propto f \quad \text{or} \quad E = hf$$

The constant of proportionality h is Planck's constant; it is $6.6 \times 10^{-34}\,\text{J}\,\text{s}$. Since

photon energy = work function + kinetic energy of fastest electrons

$$hf = \phi + \tfrac{1}{2}mv^2$$

where ϕ is the work function, and m and v are the mass and speed of the fastest electrons.

The voltage between the electrodes is equal to the potential energy per unit charge (see *Mechanics and Electricity*, Chapter 29). So the potential energy gained by an electron, as it runs up the hill repelling it back to the emitting electrode, is equal to its charge multiplied by the potential difference. If the electron just fails to reach the receiving electrode, then the potential energy it gains must be equal to the kinetic energy it was emitted with:

potential energy gained = kinetic energy lost

$$qV_s = \tfrac{1}{2}mv^2$$

where q is the charge on an electron and V_s is the **stopping voltage**. So our equation above becomes

$$hf = \phi + qV_s$$

This is Einstein's photoelectric equation. The equation can be rearranged in the form $y = mx + c$, as follows:

$$V_s = (h/q)f - \phi/q$$

A graph of V_s against f produces a straight line of gradient h/q. The charge q on an electron is known to be $1.6 \times 10^{-19}\,\text{C}$, so you can calculate Planck's constant.

Finding the threshold frequency

Look at the stopping voltage–frequency graph for caesium in Figure 28.3. As you would expect, it is a straight line. As the frequency of the radiation increases, the stopping voltage gets greater, meaning that electrons are emitted with greater energy. As the frequency gets less, the stopping voltage gets smaller, until, when the line cuts the frequency axis, electrons are emitted with zero kinetic energy. This is the **threshold frequency**. Below this frequency, no electrons are emitted.

EINSTEIN'S PHOTOELECTRIC EQUATION

Table 28.1 *Threshold frequency for a number of metals*

Metal	Threshold frequency /10^{15} Hz
caesium	0.47
sodium	0.57
zinc	0.88
chromium	1.08
iron	1.12
copper	1.13

Table 28.2 *Work function for a number of metals*

Metal	Work function /10^{-19} J	/eV
caesium	3.11	1.94
sodium	3.78	2.36
zinc	5.81	3.63
chromium	7.10	4.44
iron	7.36	4.60
copper	7.44	4.65

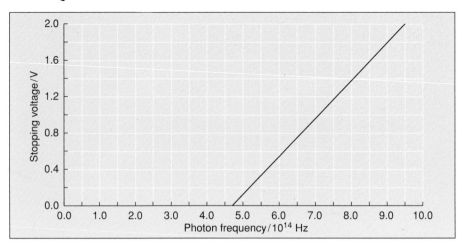

Figure 28.3   Stopping voltage for a range of frequencies

The electronvolt

The work done by a charge Q moving through a potential difference V is QV. When an electron, of charge 1.6×10^{-19} C, moves through a potential difference of 1 V, the work done is given by

$$\text{work done} = QV = 1.6 \times 10^{-19}\,\text{C} \times 1\,\text{V} = 1.6 \times 10^{-19}\,\text{J}$$

This amount of work, 1.6×10^{-19} J, is called the **electronvolt**. It is the work done when a charge equal to that on an electron moves through a potential difference of 1 V.

To convert from joules to electronvolts, divide by 1.6×10^{-19} J eV^{-1}. For example, the work function of zinc, ϕ(zinc), is

$$\phi(\text{zinc}) = 5.8 \times 10^{-19}\,\text{J} = \frac{5.8 \times 10^{-19}\,\text{J}}{1.6 \times 10^{-19}\,\text{J eV}^{-1}} = 3.6\,\text{eV}$$

The electronvolt is a conveniently sized unit of energy for photoelectricity. Tables 28.1 and 28.2 show threshold frequency and work function in both joules and electronvolts for a number of metals.

Figure 28.4   Stopping voltage for a range of photon energies

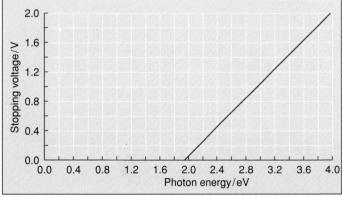

Figure 28.4 is the same graph as Figure 28.3, but the *x*-axis is labelled with photon energy in electronvolts instead of photon frequency. The intercept on the *x*-axis shows that the minimum photon energy for emission is 1.94 eV, so the work function for the emitting electrode is also 1.94 eV. For each electronvolt increase in the photon energy, the stopping voltage increases by one volt, showing that the emitted electron has an extra electronvolt of energy.

Variation of photocurrent with voltage

So far we have discussed varying the frequency of the light illuminating a photocell. If, instead, you keep the frequency constant, you can measure how photocurrent depends on the voltage between the electrodes. Figure 28.5

shows a current–voltage graph for a photocell illuminated with dim red light. As the graph shows, there is a current even when there is no voltage across the cell. The electrons have enough energy when they are emitted to travel across the gap between the electrodes even with no voltage across the cell.

At constant frequency, electrons are emitted at a constant rate, but with varying energies. With zero voltage, some will get across to the receiving electrode. Changing the voltage helps or hinders the flow. If the receiving electrode is very positive, it gives maximum help to get all the electrons across the gap, but does not cause any more to be emitted. This is **saturation**, when all the electrons that are being emitted are being received.

If the receiving electrode is negative of the emitting electrode by an amount of the stopping voltage V_s or more, it stops even the fastest electrons moving across and the current is zero.

Figure 28.6 shows the current–voltage graph for both bright and dim red light. The stopping voltages for both radiations are the same, showing that, for both radiations, electrons are emitted with the same maximum energy. This is because both the dim and bright red light have the same frequency and therefore the same photon energy.

The line for the brighter light shows a larger saturation current. More photons are arriving per second, so more electrons are emitted per second, enabling a larger maximum current.

Figure 28.7 shows current–voltage graphs for a photocell illuminated by red and blue light of the same intensity. The stopping voltage for blue light is greater than that for red, showing that the photons of blue light have a higher energy than the photons of red.

The saturation current for blue light is less than that for red, showing that there are fewer electrons emitted per second by the blue. Both radiations have the same intensity. The blue light comes as a smaller number of photons, each of which has a larger energy, emitting fewer electrons but with higher energy. The red light comes as a larger number of photons, each of which has a smaller energy, emitting more electrons but of lower energy.

Light — wave or particle?

These two chapters on quantum phenomena have shown that electromagnetic radiation behaves as though it is a stream of photons — a stream of particles. In earlier chapters, you studied the way that light behaves as a wave. This leads to something of a puzzle: Is light a wave or a particle? Perhaps the nearest simple explanation is to say that light is made of particles that have wave properties. The wave properties of the particles describe the places in which you are likely to find the particles. When two light waves interfere destructively at a point, it is not that two sets of particles arrive at the point and cancel out, but rather that the wave sets of a single particle cancel out so there is no chance of finding a particle at that point. You can read in Chapter 31 how electrons and other particles have both wave and particle properties.

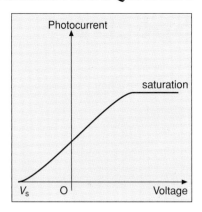

Figure 28.5   Current–voltage graph for a photocell illuminated with dim red light

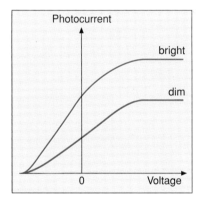

Figure 28.6   Current–voltage graphs for a photocell illuminated with two different intensities of red light

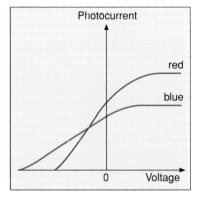

Figure 28.7   Current–voltage graphs for a photocell illuminated with different frequencies of light

29 Spectra

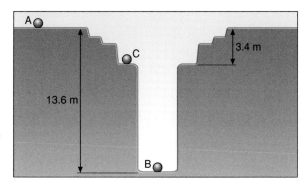

Figure 29.1   The balls have different potential energies

Stuck in a hole

Figure 29.1 shows three balls, each of weight one newton (1 N), near a hole, which has a number of levels. Ball A is free from the influence of the hole. If you use ground level as the zero for potential energy, this ball has no potential energy. Ball B is at the bottom of the hole. It is 13.6 m below ground level. It needs 1 N × 13.6 m = 13.6 J to free it from the hole. Its potential energy is 13.6 J less than that of ball A, which has an energy of 0.0 J; this is −13.6 J. Ball C is on one of the ledges around the hole. It is 3.4 m below the ground and has a potential energy of −3.4 J.

If ball C drops to the bottom of the hole, it loses 10.2 J, and its energy becomes −3.4 J − 10.2 J = −13.6 J.

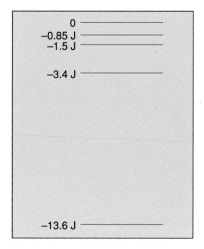

Figure 29.2   Energy level diagram

Figure 29.2 shows an energy level diagram for the hole. The diagram ignores the shape of the hole, and just shows the levels of energy that a ball in the hole can have; no other values are possible.

Electron energy levels

Electrons are held by atoms rather like the balls are held by the hole in Figure 29.1. The electron can be entirely free from the atom, in which case it is said to have zero potential energy. Or the electron can be fastened as closely as it can get to the atom. In between, there is a range of possible energy levels. In all of these energy levels, electrons have less total energy than if they were free. So these energy levels are labelled with negative values. You can use an energy level diagram to describe the possible energy states of the atom. Figure 29.3 shows an energy level diagram for the hydrogen atom, with different energies marked in electronvolts.

Normally the electron of a hydrogen atom lies in the lowest energy level–the **ground state**–like the ball lying at the bottom of the hole. But the electron can occupy any of the other possible states.

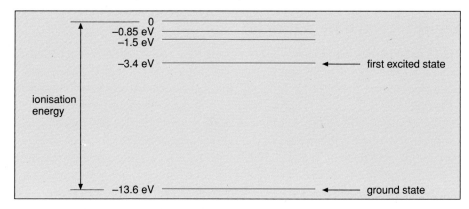

Figure 29.3   The energy levels for a hydrogen atom

Excitation and ionisation

If you give an atom energy to raise the electron above the ground state, the atom becomes **excited**. Energy is required to raise the electron above the ground state. This is **excitation energy**. The electron may remain above the ground state temporarily, but it will usually drop back to the ground state, either directly or via another level, giving out the excitation energy as it does so.

The first excitation energy for hydrogen is 10.2 eV, because it needs 10.2 eV to raise the atom from its ground state to the first excited state.

If you give the atom enough energy, you can free the electron completely from the atom. This is called **ionisation**. The **ionisation energy** is the energy required to free an electron completely, starting from the ground state of an atom. It is 13.6 eV for the hydrogen atom.

Allowable changes

The energy levels for an atom are fixed. This means that only certain transitions (changes) of energy are possible. To move between any two of these fixed levels means that the electron needs to receive, or give out, a defined amount of energy. When an atom changes from one level to a lower one, the surplus energy E is given out as a single photon of radiation. The defined changes of energy mean that there are defined frequencies of radiation given out, since $E = hf$. These frequencies therefore give information about the energy levels in an atom.

The change in energy E of an electron is the difference in energy of the two states between which the electron moves, $E = E_2 - E_1$. The frequency of the emitted radiation is given by the formula $E = hf$. So

$$hf = E_2 - E_1$$

Big jumps mean large energy changes, which correspond to high frequencies of radiation with short wavelengths. Small jumps mean small energy changes, which correspond to low frequencies of radiation with long wavelengths.

The atoms of each element have a characteristic set of energy levels, and so give out a characteristic set of frequencies of radiation when they are excited. So you can identify an element from the frequencies of the radiation it emits when excited.

Observing spectra

- Put a slit in front of a hydrogen lamp. Hold a diffraction grating next to your eye and look through it at the slit (Figure 29.4).
- Sketch the pattern of light you see.
- Repeat with lamps containing different elements.

Figure 29.4   Using a diffraction grating to observe an emission spectrum

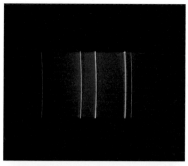

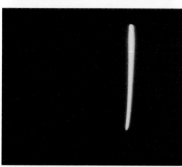

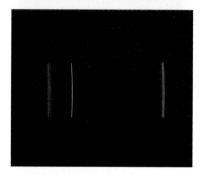

Emission spectra

You can give an element energy to excite the atoms by heating it. In this way, electrons are continually being given energy to enable them to rise to a higher state, but they then fall down again. The atoms give out the range of frequencies characteristic of that element. This range of frequencies of emitted radiations is called the **emission spectrum** of the atom.

Chemists can identify many metals just by putting a sample in a flame and identifying the characteristic spectrum by eye.

Using a diffraction grating to observe spectra

A diffraction grating works on the same principle as Young's slits (see Chapter 25). But the grating has more slits and they are closer together, so the fringes are brighter and spaced much further apart. You can use a diffraction grating to observe and measure the wavelengths of radiation from an emission spectrum. Figure 29.5 shows how you can observe the fringes that a diffraction grating can produce on the retina of the eye.

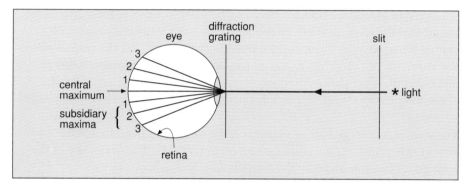

Figure 29.6   Emission spectra from (top) cadmium, (centre) sodium, (bottom) hydrogen

Figure 29.5   Superposition fringes on the back of the eye

Figure 29.6 shows the emission spectra of some common elements, including that of hydrogen. Notice the series of discrete lines, which correspond to the series of discrete energy levels in the atom.

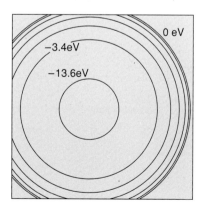

Figure 29.7   Bohr atom

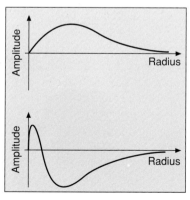

Figure 29.8   Schrödinger atom

Standing waves in atoms

Neils Bohr suggested that the discrete energy levels in atoms are due to the electrons being allowed to have discrete orbits around the atom, rather like Figure 29.7. The changes in energy correspond to changes in orbit.

Erwin Schrödinger suggested that the energy levels in atoms were due to electrons behaving like standing waves in the atom, with a profile like the waves in Figure 29.8. Only certain types of wave fit the atom, and these correspond to the fixed energy states.

The electromagnetic spectrum

The electromagnetic spectrum comprises a wide range of electromagnetic waves (Table 30.1). All the waves consist of transverse oscillating electric and magnetic waves. Electromagnetic waves can be polarised. They all travel at the same speed of $3.00 \times 10^8\,\text{m s}^{-1}$ in a vacuum.

Table 30.1 *The electromagnetic spectrum*

Type	Frequency	Wavelength	How made	Uses	Photon energy
long-wave radio	~250 kHz	~1200 m	oscillating currents in aerials	radio	~10^{-28} J
medium-wave radio	~1000 kHz (1 MHz)	~300 m	oscillating currents in aerials	radio	~10^{-27} J
short-wave radio	~10 MHz	~30 m	oscillating currents in aerials	radio	~10^{-26} J
VHF	~100 MHz	~3 m	oscillating currents in aerials	radio	~10^{-25} J
UHF	~400 MHz	~1 m	oscillating currents in aerials	television	~10^{-25} J
microwaves	~2.5 GHz	~10 cm	directly produced in waveguides	radar, cooking, communicating	~10^{-24} J
infra-red	~10^{14} Hz	~1 μm (>700 nm)	hot bodies, LEDs	night-sights, heating, short-distance communication	~10^{-19} J ~1 eV
visible	~5×10^{14} Hz	700 – 400 nm	very hot bodies, LEDs	seeing, etc	2 – 3 eV
ultra-violet	>7.5×10^{14} Hz	<400 nm	extremely hot bodies, sparks, discharge tubes	sun-tanning, detecting invisible marking, sterilising	>3 eV
X-rays	~10^{18} Hz	~10^{-10} m	stopping fast electrons	X-raying people and materials	~10 000 eV
gamma rays (overlap with X-rays)	~10^{20} Hz	~10^{-12} m	nuclear decay	X-raying thick objects, killing cancerous cells, sterilising	~1 MeV ~10^{-13} J
cosmic rays	very high	very short	from distant parts of the Universe	just cause a hazard	up to tens of joules

Matter waves

Crossed gratings

- Shine a laser beam into a single diffraction grating and look at the pattern produced on the screen.
- Then use two gratings at right angles and look at the pattern due to that.
- Next put a number of gratings at a range of angles to each other (Figure 31.1) and look at the pattern that this produces.

LASER BEAM

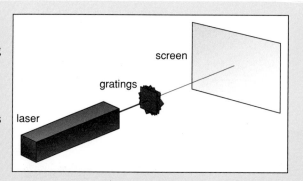

Figure 31.1   Producing superposition patterns from a number of crossed gratings

Figure 31.2   The superposition pattern for one grating

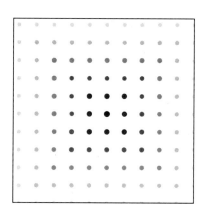

Figure 31.3   The superposition pattern for two crossed gratings

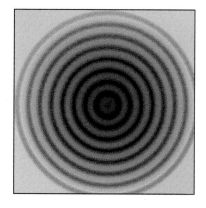

Figure 31.4   The superposition pattern for many gratings at different angles

Diffraction patterns

Figure 31.2 shows the fringe pattern produced when you shine a laser onto a single diffraction grating. Figure 31.3 shows what happens with two gratings at right angles. The second grating diffracts each of the maxima from the first grating to produce an array of dots. If you use many gratings at many different angles, you get a fuzzy series of rings caused by the diffraction patterns of each different grating, as Figure 31.4 shows.

Electron diffraction

When you fire electrons at graphite, you might expect them to be scattered through a range of angles to produce a fuzzy patch on the screen. Although this does happen, the pattern produced on the screen is not a single patch of varying brightness but in fact consists of a series of rings, as shown in Figure 31.6. There are places on the screen where many electrons hit, and places where no electrons hit. This pattern is like the diffraction pattern produced by a series of gratings at angles in a light beam. If a beam of electrons behaved like a beam of particles, you would expect them to arrive at all parts of the screen. In fact the beam of electrons behaves more like a beam of light. There seem to be destructive superposition effects, which means that there are some places on the screen where no electrons arrive. These observations, and others like them, lead to the idea that electrons have wave properties.

Finding electron wavelength

You know from Chapter 25 that you can calculate the wavelength λ from a Young's slits experiment using the formula $\lambda = xs/D$, where x, s and D are the fringe width, slit separation and screen distance, respectively. You can use this formula to find the wavelength of light travelling through a series of gratings that are producing diffraction rings. As Figure 31.6 shows, you can also use it to measure the wavelength of the electrons diffracted by a piece of graphite.

Firing electrons at graphite

- Figure 31.5 shows an electron beam tube. The low-voltage power supply heats up the cathode and so gives the atoms enough energy for them to emit electrons. You might like to compare this **thermionic emission** with photoelectric emission. The EHT power supply attracts the electrons from the filament to a positive plate, which has a piece of graphite fixed in the middle. The fluorescent screen gives out light whenever it is hit by electrons, and therefore shows what happens after the electrons hit the graphite.
- Observe the pattern produced when the electrons hit the screen. Then change the voltage of the EHT power supply and see how the pattern changes

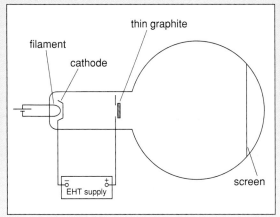

Figure 31.5   An electron diffraction tube

The layers of atoms in graphite produce electron superposition patterns. These layers are 2.1×10^{-10} m apart, and this is equivalent to the Young's slit separation. The screen is 0.14 m from the graphite, and the first subsidiary maximum is at a distance of 12 mm from the centre. So using $\lambda = xs/D$, we get

$$\lambda = (1.2 \times 10^{-2}\,\text{m} \times 2.1 \times 10^{-10}\,\text{m})/0.14\,\text{m} = 1.8 \times 10^{-11}\,\text{m}$$

De Broglie's theorem

The French physicist, Louis Victor de Broglie (pronounced "de Broy') suggested that electrons, like other particles, have wave properties, with a wavelength that is dependent on the momentum of the particle. His equation states that

$$\lambda = \frac{h}{p}$$

where λ is the wavelength, h is Planck's constant and p is the momentum (found by multiplying the mass by the velocity). We can use this relationship to calculate the wavelength of the electrons producing the superposition pattern shown in Figure 31.6 and compare the result with the value above.

Calculating the electron momentum

As the high-voltage power supply accelerates the electrons, the energy it gives them is their charge $\times$ the accelerating voltage. This is equal to their kinetic energy:

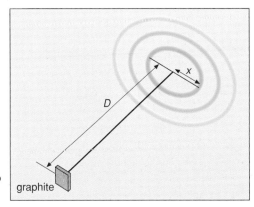

Figure 31.6   Ring geometry

$$\text{kinetic energy} = \text{charge} \times \text{voltage}$$

$$\tfrac{1}{2}mv^2 = qV$$

and therefore

$$v^2 = 2qV/m \qquad \text{so} \qquad v = \sqrt{(2qV/m)}$$

For an electron, $m = 9.1 \times 10^{-31}\,\text{kg}$ and $q = 1.6 \times 10^{-19}\,\text{C}$. The electrons in Figure 31.6 were accelerated through 5000 V. Therefore

$$
\begin{aligned}
v &= \sqrt{[(2 \times 1.6 \times 10^{-19}\,\text{C} \times 5000\,\text{V})/(9.1 \times 10^{-31}\,\text{kg})]} \\
&= 4.2 \times 10^7\,\text{m s}^{-1}
\end{aligned}
$$

and momentum $= mv$ is given as

$$mv = 9.1 \times 10^{-31}\,\text{kg} \times 4.2 \times 10^7\,\text{m s}^{-1} = 3.8 \times 10^{-23}\,\text{kg m s}^{-1}$$

De Broglie's equation states that for a particle with this momentum

$$\lambda = h/p = (6.6 \times 10^{-34}\,\text{J s})/(3.8 \times 10^{-23}\,\text{kg m s}^{-1}) = 1.7 \times 10^{-11}\,\text{m}$$

which is in close agreement with the measurement above.

If you increase the accelerating voltage, the momentum of the electrons increases, so the wavelength decreases. The width of the fringes decreases and the rings close up on the screen.

Two-slit diffraction with electrons

Figure 31.7 shows how you can demonstrate two-slit superposition with electrons. This arrangement is just like Young's slits for light, but the superposition is harder to demonstrate. The wavelength even for very fast electrons is small, so the slits need to be very close for fringes to be observable.

All matter has wave properties

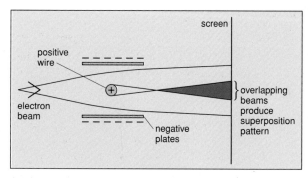

Figure 31.7   Two-slit superposition with electrons

De Broglie's theory about the wave properties of particles applies to all particles, even large ones like people. The theory suggests that particles are indeed separate particles and that the wave that is associated with them (called their *wave function*) describes the probability of finding the particle in a particular place. Practice question 31.3 invites you to calculate the wavelength of a creeping bacterium. Even for that small particle, the wavelength is much smaller than the length of the bacterium, so the wave effects are simply not observable. Wave properties are only significant for particles of the size of an atom or smaller.

Practice questions

Chapter 1

1.1 Explain why a metre rule with a resolution of 1 mm may have an accuracy of only 4 mm.

1.2 Describe how you would measure the thickness of the pages in this textbook using a micrometer.

1.3 The thickness of a coin is found to be 1.23 mm. If the uncertainty in this reading is 0.05 mm, calculate the percentage uncertainty.

Chapter 2

2.1 Describe how you would measure the density of an irregularly shaped solid object that is known to have a greater density than that of water. Explain how your method would have to be adapted if the object's density was less than that of water.

2.2 VHS video tape is 1.25 cm wide, 20 μm thick and has a density of 800 kg m^{-3}. A fully wound spool consists of a central spindle with a radius of 1 cm surrounded by sufficient tape to bring the total radius up to 4 cm. Calculate the mass of tape present. If the tape runs for three hours, estimate the speed at which it feeds past the tape-head. (Ignore the fact that the tape-head is also moving as this happens.)

2.3 A hydraulic press has a large circular piston of radius 96 cm and a circular plunger of radius 6 cm. Calculate (a) the upward force exerted on the piston when a force of 150 N is used to push the plunger down, and (b) the distance that the piston moves up when the plunger moves down 64 cm.

Chapter 3

3.1 Compare and contrast the arrangements of the particles in solids, liquids and gases.

3.2 With reference to different materials, explain the meanings of the terms *crystalline*, *polycrystalline* and *amorphous*.

3.3 Describe how a piece of balloon rubber can be used to demonstrate that rubber is amorphous until it is stretched, when it becomes crystalline.

Chapter 4

4.1 A single spring is found to extend elastically by 12 cm when supporting a mass of 300 g. Calculate its spring constant. Find the total extension produced when three of these springs are joined in series and used to support a mass of 600 g. What would be the total extension if the three springs were used in parallel to support the 600 g mass?

4.2 Sketch a graph to show how force F varies with extension x for a spring that obeys Hooke's law. Use this graph to help explain why the energy stored in the spring is $\frac{1}{2}Fx$. When a mass of 400 g is hung on a certain spring, it extends the spring by 4 cm. Calculate the elastic potential energy stored in the spring.

Chapter 5

5.1 Sketch a graph that shows how the length of a rubber cord varies with the tension in the cord as the tension increases from zero until the cord breaks. Account for the shape of the curve you have drawn in terms of the molecular structure of rubber.

5.2 When a wire is stretched, it behaves at first *elastically* and then *plastically* until it finally breaks. Sketch a force–extension graph for such a wire, indicating the two types of behaviour. Explain what happens to the structure of the wire in each case and relate this to the wire's behaviour if the force were removed during the stretching process.

5.3 Compare the behaviour of a *brittle* material with that of a *tough* material.

Chapter 6

6.1 Calculate: (a) the stress in a hair of diameter 50 μm when it has a 40 g mass suspended from it; (b) the total length of a 9 cm elastic band when extended to a strain of 400%; and (c) the maximum force that a 10 mm diameter metal bar can withstand if the maximum permissible tensile stress for this metal bar is 80 MN m^{-2}.

6.2 Describe in detail the experiment (involving a dual-suspension technique) that you would use to accurately determine the Young modulus for steel in the form of a wire.

6.3 A metal bar of length 1.5 m has a square cross-section of side 35 mm. When a tensile force of 7 kN is applied, it extends elastically by 0.64 mm. Calculate: (a) the stress applied, (b) the strain produced, and (c) the Young modulus of the metal.

PRACTICE QUESTIONS

Chapter 7

7.1 Draw a diagram of the experimental arrangement used in the alpha particle scattering experiment. Describe the observations that led to the discovery of the nucleus.

7.2 The 'symbol' $^{197}_{79}$Au represents an atom of gold-197. State (a) the number of protons in its nucleus, (b) the number of nucleons in its nucleus, and (c) the number of neutrons in its nucleus. The density of gold is $18\,880\,\mathrm{kg\,m^{-3}}$. Explain why the density of nuclear matter is very much greater than this value.

7.3 What are *isotopes* of an element? Tin has 25 isotopes, of which the lightest is represented by the symbol $^{108}_{50}$Sn. Knowing that all possible isotopes of tin exist, write down the symbol for the heaviest one.

Chapter 8

8.1 Describe how you would use a GM tube, a counter and a method involving penetrating power to check that a potassium salt emits only beta particles.

8.2 $^{216}_{84}$Po decays to lead (Pb) with the emission of an alpha (α) particle. The lead then emits gamma (γ) radiation before decaying to bismuth (Bi) with the emission of a beta-minus (β⁻) particle. Write down the nuclear equation for each of these three decays. The above sequence forms part of the thorium decay series, which begins with thorium-232 and ends with lead-208, which is stable. How many alpha particle decays occur in the thorium decay series?

8.3 Sketch how the paths of alpha, beta and gamma radiations travelling from left to right are affected by a magnetic field that acts North to South into the paper. Give reasons for the different shapes of the paths that you have drawn. Compare the shapes and directions of these paths with those followed in an electric field.

Chapter 9

9.1 $^{241}_{94}$Pu (plutonium) decays via β⁻, α, α, β⁻, α, α, β⁻, α, α, α, β⁻, α, β⁻ to $^{209}_{83}$Bi (bismuth). Draw a *N–Z* diagram of the complete decay chain.

9.2 Sketch the graph of binding energy per nucleon against nucleon number. With reference to your graph, distinguish between the processes of *nuclear fission* and *nuclear fusion*.

Chapter 10

10.1 Define the terms *half-life* and *decay constant*.

10.2 Describe the experiment that you would use to determine accurately the decay constant of a radioactive source that is known to have a half-life of about a minute.

If a decay process starts with N_0 atoms, how many atoms of that nuclide will be present when $t = t_{\frac{1}{2}}$? Substitute these 'values' into the equation $N = N_0 e^{-\lambda t}$ to find the relation between λ and $t_{\frac{1}{2}}$. The decay constant of a radioactive isotope of strontium is $7.84 \times 10^{-10}\,\mathrm{s^{-1}}$. Show that its half-life is approximately 28 years. A source initially contains $4.5\,\mathrm{\mu g}$ of this strontium isotope. Calculate the mass of this isotope that will remain after (a) 84 years and (b) 14 years.

Chapter 11

11.1 Explain the terms amplitude, period and frequency.

11.2 The graph shows how the displacement of an oscillating body varies with time.

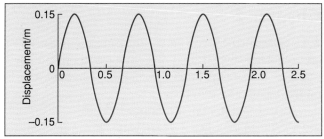

State the amplitude of these oscillations. Determine their frequency. Copy the graph and mark all the points where the body has zero speed.

Chapter 12

12.1 Define *simple harmonic motion*.

12.2 A particle moves with simple harmonic motion between the points A and C as shown.

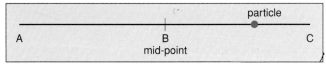

At which point (or points) will the particle have (a) zero velocity, (b) zero acceleration, (c) maximum velocity to the right, (d) maximum acceleration to the left, and (e) maximum kinetic energy.

Chapter 13

13.1 An oscillator moves in such a way that its displacement x, measured in centimetres, varies with time t according to the equation $x = 8\cos(4\pi t)$. What are the values of its amplitude, frequency and period? Sketch three 'vertically aligned' graphs to show how its displacement, velocity and acceleration vary with time during the initial two seconds of its motion. Calculate the oscillator's maximum velocity and its maximum acceleration.

13.2 Two runners are taking part in a long-distance endurance race around a circular track. They start together (in phase) and proceed with constant lap times of 84 s and 89 s respectively. How long will elapse before the faster runner is half a lap in front of (out of phase with) the slower runner?

Chapter 14

14.1   A light helical spring hangs vertically from a firm support. An 800 g mass is attached to the lower end of the spring and produces a static extension of 4.0 cm. Calculate the spring constant of the spring, and the period of the 800 g mass when it performs small vertical oscillations.

14.2   Explain why a clock can be designed around a system executing simple harmonic motion. Give one example of such an oscillating system.

Chapter 15

15.1   The natural frequency f of a pendulum of mass m and length L is given by: $f = \frac{1}{(2\pi)}\sqrt{\frac{g}{L}}$. Explain what is meant by *natural frequency*. Show that the natural frequency equation is homogeneous with respect to its units. For what value of L would the pendulum have a natural frequency of 1.0 Hz? What is the most useful characteristic of a pendulum?

15.2   The drums of an automatic washing machine are

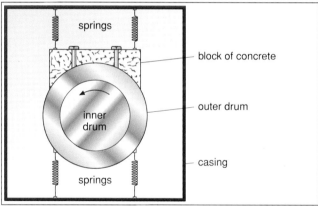

attached to the casing by strong springs as shown. The inner drum rotates within the outer drum at variable speeds according to the washing programme. The total mass of the two drums is 25 kg. A block of concrete of mass 35 kg is added to the outer drum. The natural period of oscillation of the system is 2 s. Calculate the effective spring constant of this mass–spring system. When the washing machine enters the spin part of its programme, the inner drum starts from rest, building up rotational speed gradually. As the speed increases, the system is observed to oscillate with an increasing amplitude, reaching a maximum value of 3 cm, before decreasing again at higher speeds. Why does the system

oscillate when the inner drum is rotated? How many revolutions per minute will the inner drum be making when the maximum amplitude of oscillation is observed? Explain your answer. Sketch a graph showing how the amplitude of the system varies with the frequency of rotation of the inner drum. State and explain one effect on the oscillations of running the machine without the block of concrete fixed to the outer drum.

Chapter 16

16.1   Describe how a continuous plane (straight) water wave can be produced in the laboratory. How could the frequency of the water wave be changed? How would you measure the wavelength of the water wave and its wave speed?

16.2   What is meant by the term *energy flux*? The inverse square law can be applied to the energy flux of electromagnetic waves produced by a point source. Describe what is meant by an *inverse square law*. Explain how such a law automatically arises from uniform energy propagation from a point source, stating the principle that has to be applied. Solar radiation arrives at the Earth's orbit at the rate of 1.4 kW m^{-2}. If the average radius of the Earth's orbit around the Sun is 1.49×10^{11} m, calculate the power output of the Sun.

Chapter 17

17.1   Sound waves are *longitudinal* while those on the surface of water are mainly *transverse*. In what way do these two types of wave differ? How would you demonstrate that sound waves moving through air are longitudinal?

17.2   Visible light and microwaves can both be polarised. Explain the term *plane polarised wave*. How would you demonstrate that microwaves from a given source are plane polarised? Describe how you would test whether or not reflected visible light is plane polarised.

Chapter 18

18.1   A typical value for the speed of sound in air is 330 m s^{-1}. A tuning fork emits a continuous burst of waves that have a wavelength of 8.5 cm. The tuning fork vibrates for a total time of 6.5 s. Calculate (a) the frequency of the emitted sound, (b) the number of complete waves emitted during 20 ms, and (c) the total length of the wavetrain emitted.

18.2   The diagram shows part of a transverse wave travelling from left to right at one instant in time.

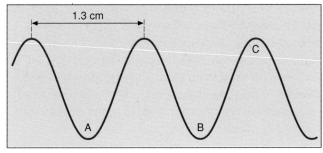

The frequency of its source is 20 Hz. A and B are molecules that at this instant are in neighbouring troughs, 1.3 cm apart. C is on a crest. Calculate the speed at which the wave is travelling. Copy the sketch and add to it the new position of the wave after a further 12.5 ms. Mark the new positions of the molecules A, B and C. Sketch a graph showing how the displacement of molecule A varies with time for 100 ms from the instant shown in the above sketch. Which of the three molecules are vibrating 'in phase' and which are 'in antiphase'.

Chapter 19

19.1   Sketch the diffraction pattern produced when laser light passes through a narrow slit. Compare the widths of the fringes observed.

19.2   Describe, with the aid of a clearly labelled diagram, how you would demonstrate for microwaves that the angle of incidence is equal to the angle of reflection. Explain why it is more difficult to test the laws of reflection for microwaves than for visible light. How would you test the laws of reflection using sound waves?

Chapter 20

20.1   A ray of light, initially in air, is refracted at a plane glass surface at a gradually increasing angle of incidence, θ_1. For each incident angle, the value of the corresponding angle of refraction, θ_2, is measured. What would you plot in order to obtain a straight-line graph relating θ_1 and θ_2?

20.2   A large tray holds water that is deep to the left of the straight line AB shown and shallow to its right.

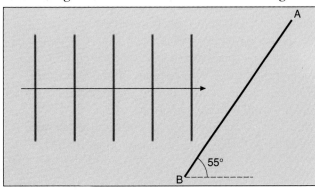

The deep water wave speed is 28 cm s^{-1}, which reduces to 21 cm s^{-1} in the shallow water. Copy and complete the diagram to show clearly the wavefronts as they pass over the boundary and into the shallow region.

20.3   A lifeguard, who can run four times as fast on soft sand as she can swim in the sea, stands on a beach 15 m from the water's edge. She sees that a swimmer, 30 m further along the beach, is in difficulty out in the sea. Being a good physicist, she quickly calculates the best path to follow and sets off aiming for the water's edge at a point that is 20 m further along the beach. How far out from the water's edge is the swimmer?

Chapter 21

21.1   The refractive indices of air, glass and water are 1.00, 1.50 and 1.33 respectively. Calculate the angle of refraction when a ray of light is incident at an angle of 35° when travelling from (a) air to glass, (b) water to air, and (c) glass to water.

21.2   A narrow parallel beam of white light strikes the mid-point of the side of a 60° prism at an angle of incidence greater than 30°. Draw a diagram showing what happens to the light as it passes into the prism and out of the far side. Explain, with references to your diagram, the meaning of the terms *refraction*, *deviation* and *dispersion*.

Chapter 22

22.1   Explain the terms *critical angle* and *total internal reflection*. Calculate the critical angle for the boundary between the deep and shallow water in question 20.2.

22.2   A ray of light enters a block of transparent material through the mid-point of one of its sides, at an angle of incidence of 85° as shown.

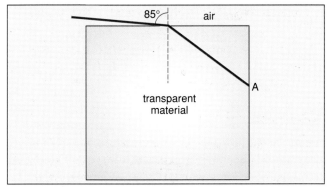

The block is a square of side 6 cm. The refractive index of the transparent material is 1.40. Calculate the distance from point A to the top right-hand corner of the block, and the angle between the normal and the ray as it leaves the block at A. When a similar block with a refractive index of 1.50 is used, the ray of light fails to emerge from the right-hand side of the block. Why does this happen? Sketch the path taken by the ray of light in this case.

22.3 The graph shows the variation in the refractive index across a diameter of a step-index multimode optical fibre.

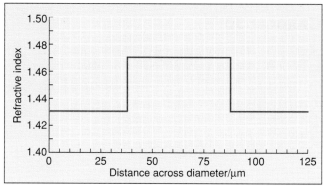

Why is this design of optical fibre known as a 'step-index' type? What is the diameter of its core? Calculate the critical angle of the boundary between the core and the cladding. Explain the 'multimode nature' of such an optical fibre. What effect will the multimode nature have on the signal received at the end of a long fibre optic cable? The cladding and the core of a monomode optical fibre have refractive indices of 1.41 and 1.49 respectively. Sketch a graph showing how the refractive index varies across its diameter. Such a monomode cable has a length of 25 km. How long will a pulse of light take to travel along its full length?

Chapter 23

23.1 State the *principle of superposition*. Explain in terms of the phase of the waves involved the existence of destructive and constructive superposition.

23.2 What are coherent sources? Explain why two sources are unable to produce a stable superposition pattern unless they have the same frequency. Two sources are found to produce a stable and well-defined superposition pattern. What additional fact does this tell you about the two sources?

Chapter 24

24.1 Two loudspeakers are connected to a 2 kHz supply and placed 2 m apart at the front of a laboratory. Students walk around the room and find that there is a minimum intensity along a line that is equidistant from both loudspeakers. What does this tell you about the

way in which the two loudspeakers are connected? How must the apparatus be adjusted to produce a central maximum along this same line?

24.2 The diagram shows microwaves arriving at a receiver R having travelled along two different paths from the same transmitter T.

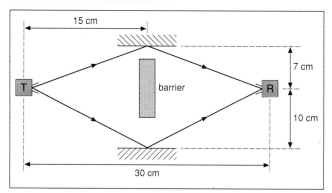

Explain whether or not these waves will be coherent. The wavelength of the microwaves is 2.9 cm. Is the receiver shown detecting a maximum or a minimum intensity?

Chapter 25

25.1 Explain why a small slit is placed in front of a filament lamp that is being used to produce superposition patterns.

25.2 Draw a diagram of the apparatus that you would use to produce a two-slit superposition pattern for monochromatic visible light. Mark any relevant dimensions on your diagram. Sketch the superposition pattern produced.

25.3 A red light produces a wavelength of 680 nm. The superposition pattern produced on a screen 1.8 m from the double slit has a fringe width of 3.2 mm. Calculate the slit separation of the double slit.

Chapter 26

26.1 What conditions are required for the production of a stationary wave? Explain how *nodes* and *antinodes* are formed.

26.2 Two loudspeakers are connected to the same oscillator and placed facing each other several metres apart. The oscillator produces a frequency of 850 Hz. The speed of sound in air is 330 m s⁻¹. Calculate the separation of adjacent nodes along the line joining the two loudspeakers. A small microphone is moved at a constant speed along this line. It records a signal whose intensity varies periodically at 5 Hz. What is the speed of the microphone?

PRACTICE QUESTIONS

Chapter 27

27.1 What is meant by *photoelectric emission*. Describe, in detail, how you would use a zinc plate and an electroscope, together with other apparatus, to illustrate this effect.

27.2 Explain why, for a given surface, there is a maximum wavelength of incident radiation above which photoelectric emission cannot be observed. The magnitude of this maximum wavelength increases slightly if the temperature of the photoelectric surface is increased. Suggest a reason for this.

27.3 What is a *photon*? In terms of photons, what is the difference between (a) a bright light source and a dim one of the same frequency, and (b) a visible light source and an ultra-violet source of the same intensity? Why does photoelectric emission occur from zinc with a weak ultra-violet source, but not with an intense visible source?

Chapter 28

28.1 The work function for sodium metal is 3.78×10^{-19} J. Explain the term *work function*. A fresh sodium surface is irradiated with ultra-violet light of wavelength 319 nm. Calculate the maximum kinetic energy of the emitted photoelectrons. When photoelectric emission is occurring, what determines (a) the number of photoelectrons released each second, and (b) the maximum kinetic energy of the emitted photoelectrons?

28.2 A certain material has a work function of 1.35 eV. Calculate the longest wavelength of incident radiation that can cause photoelectrons to be emitted from the surface of this material. The surface is illuminated with light of wavelength 0.4 μm. Calculate the maximum velocity with which photoelectrons will be emitted. What potential difference will be required to just stop these photoelectrons leaving the surface?

Chapter 29

29.1 The *ionisation energy* for a mercury atom in its *ground state* is 10.4 eV, while 5.5 eV is required to ionise a mercury atom that is in its first *excited state*. Explain the terms *ionisation energy*, *ground state* and *excited state*. Before electrons in an electron beam can collide inelastically with the mercury atoms in mercury gas at room temperature, the electrons must have energies of at least 4.9 eV. Explain the difference between an *elastic* and an *inelastic* collision. Calculate the minimum speed of an electron capable of having an inelastic collision with a mercury atom. What wavelength of electromagnetic radiation is emitted by a mercury atom following an inelastic collision with an electron of energy 4.9 eV?

29.2 When light of wavelength λ passes through a diffraction grating that has N slits per metre, the nth-order spectrum is deviated through an angle θ such that $n\lambda = (\sin\theta)/N$. Show that this equation is homogeneous with respect to its units. Describe how you would use a diffraction grating to observe an emission spectrum.

Chapter 30

30.1 Describe, with the aid of a sketch graph, the form of an electromagnetic wave. The electromagnetic spectrum consists of seven main divisions—three of these are given in the table below:

radio waves	(a)	(b)	visible	(c)	(d)	gamma rays

Give the names of the divisions represented by the letters (a)–(d). State the *decreasing* quantity associated with a left-to-right movement across the above spectrum. In which division would you find a wavelength of (a) 3 cm and (b) 600 nm?

30.2 A radio transmitter emits a wave of frequency 909 kHz at a power of 12 kW. Calculate the energy of a photon of this radiation and the photon flux (number of photons per second) produced by the transmitter. Assuming that the transmitter acts as a point source, calculate the photon flux density (photon flux per unit area) at a distance of 20 km from the transmitter.

Chapter 31

31.1 Explain, with reference to the behaviour of both light photons and high-speed electrons, what you understand by the phrase *wave–particle duality*. Give examples of both types of behaviour in each case.

31.2 Calculate (a) the speed, momentum and de Broglie wavelength of an electron with an energy of 150 eV, and (b) the spacing of the slits of the diffraction grating required to give a first-order 'electron' image at an angle of 12° to the direct beam for electrons of this energy. How might such a grating spacing be achieved?

31.3 An electron has a speed of 4×10^7 m s^{-1}. Calculate its wavelength. An extremely thin and slow student (mass 7 kg!) has a speed of 3 μm s^{-1}. Calculate his wavelength. Repeat the calculation for a creeping bacterium (mass 10^{-15} kg) to find why even tiny creatures do not diffract. Why is the electron diffracted by a carbon lattice of spacing 10^{-9} m, but diffraction of the student is not noticeable when he goes through a door 0.5 m wide?

Examination questions

1 (a) Using the kinetic theory, describe briefly one way in which gases are similar to liquids but different from solids. [2]

In similar terms, describe one way in which liquids are similar to solids but different from gases. [2]

(b) The diagram shows two linked cylinders with internal diameters of 12 mm and 5 mm respectively. A force of 50 N is applied to the piston in the narrow cylinder. The space between the pistons is filled with water.

Calculate the magnitude of the force F exerted by the larger piston. [3]

2 The graph shows the behaviour of a material A subjected to a tensile stress.

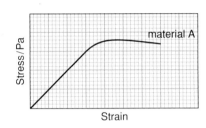

How would you obtain the Young modulus of material A from the graph? [2]

What is the unit of the Young modulus? [1]

Copy the graph. On your graph, draw a second line to show the behaviour of a material B which has a *greater* Young modulus and is brittle. Draw a third line to show the behaviour of a material C which has a *lower* value of Young modulus and whose behaviour becomes plastic at a lower strain. [3]

3 Rubber is commonly described as being more elastic than steel but steel has a greater modulus of elasticity than rubber. Sketch two stress–strain graphs, on the same axes, which illustrate the difference in behaviour of rubber and steel when subjected to stress. [4]

Describe with the aid of diagrams the difference in molecular structure of rubber and steel. [4]

4 Geiger and Marsden carried out an experiment with a fine beam of alpha particles directed normally on to a thin gold film. The experiment showed that most of the alpha particles go straight through the gold film with undiminished speed, and that a small proportion of them are strongly deflected.

State *two* conclusions which can be deduced from these results. [2+2]

5 $^{12}_{6}\text{C}$ and $^{14}_{6}\text{C}$ are two isotopes of carbon.

State the number of electrons in a neutral atom of $^{14}_{6}\text{C}$. [1]

State the number of neutrons in a neutral atom of $^{14}_{6}\text{C}$. [1]

$^{14}_{6}\text{C}$ decays by beta emission. Copy and complete the nuclear equation below:

$$^{14}_{6}\text{C} \rightarrow \text{N} + \text{e}$$

[2]

Describe briefly how you would test whether $^{14}_{6}C$ decays only by beta emission. [3]

6 The isotope $^{22}_{11}Na$ decays into a nucleus X by beta-plus emission with a half-life of 2.6 years. Complete the nuclear equation below:

$$^{22}_{11}Na \rightarrow \overset{22}{\underset{10}{}}X + \overset{0}{\underset{1}{}}\beta$$ [2]

Calculate the number of nuclei in 0.22 g of $^{22}_{11}Na$ and hence find the activity of 0.22 g of $^{22}_{11}Na$. [5]

State one precaution you would take in an experiment to obtain a reliable value for a half-life of this magnitude. [1]

7 (a) The graph shows the variation of N, the neutron number of a nuclide, with Z, the proton number of the nuclide. The curved line represents the mean or average variation for stable nuclei up to uranium, U; the broken line is simply a plot of $N = Z$.

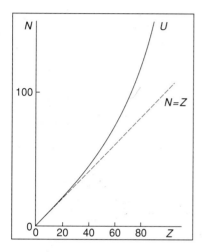

Copy the graph. Mark the following on your graph.

   (i) An α to show any point which could represent an unstable nucleus which would tend to decay by α emission.

   (ii) A β^- to show any point which could represent an unstable nucleus which would tend to decay by β^- emission. [2]

   (b) Mass of a proton = 1.0078 u
   Mass of a neutron = 1.0087 u
   Mass of $^{238}_{92}U$ nucleus = 238.0508 u

Use the data above to calculate the difference between the mass of a $^{238}_{92}U$ nucleus and the total mass of its separate nucleons. [3]

Hence calculate the total binding energy of a $^{238}_{92}U$ nucleus. [2]

8 Define simple harmonic motion. [2]

The curve labelled A shows how the displacement of a body executing simple harmonic motion varies with time.

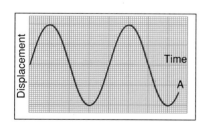

Copy the graph. Add the following to your graph:

   (i) A curve labelled B showing how the acceleration of the same body varies with time over the same time period.

   (ii) A curve labelled C showing how the velocity of the same body varies with time over the same time period. [4]

Which pair of curves illustrates the definition of simple harmonic motion? Explain your answer. [1+2]

9 The diagram shows a mass of 0.51 kg suspended at the lower end of a spring. The graph shows how the tension, F, in the spring varies with the extension, Δx, of the spring.

Use the graph to find a value for the spring constant *k*. [2]

The mass, originally at point O, is set into small vertical oscillations between the points A and B. Choose A, B or O to complete the following sentences.

The speed of the mass is a maximum when the mass is at ... . The velocity and acceleration are both in the same direction when the mass is moving from ... to ... . [2]

Calculate the period of oscillation *T* of the mass. [2]

What energy transformations take place while the mass moves from B to O? [2]

10 A 60 W light bulb converts electrical energy to visible light with an efficiency of 8%. Calculate the visible light intensity 2 m away from the light bulb. [3]

The average energy of the photons emitted by the light bulb in the visible region is 2 eV. Calculate the number of these photons received per square metre per second at this distance from the light bulb. [2]

11 The diagram shows a ray of monochromatic light incident on a triangular glass prism (refractive index = 1.50) at an angle of incidence θ_1. The light just emerges from the face PR of the prism.

Calculate:

    (i)   the speed of light in the prism,

    (ii) the value of the angle θ_c,

    (iii) the value of the angle θ_1. [4]

θ_1 is the minimum incident angle for light of this wavelength to just emerge from the prism. Explain why this is so. [2]

Copy the diagram. On your diagram, draw the path that would be followed by a ray of light of a lower frequency at the same angle of incidence. [2]

12 Draw a diagram showing one situation in which you would observe dispersion of light. Explain why the dispersion occurs in the way you have shown in your diagram. [5]

13 (a) The diagram shows an optical fibre with light entering at an angle such that it *just* undergoes total internal reflection at the surface between the core and the cladding.

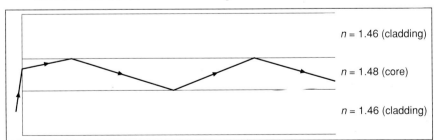

Calculate the critical angle for the interface between the core and the cladding. [2]

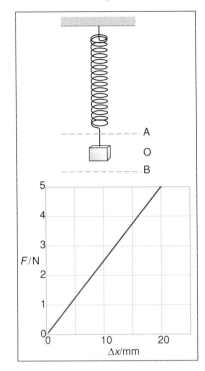

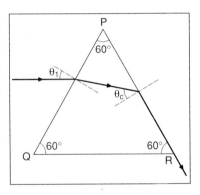

EXAMINATION QUESTIONS

(b) In optical fibres the refractive index of the core and cladding are very similar. Explain why this is necessary. [3]

14 The diagram shows an arrangement to produce superposition fringes by Young's two-slits method.

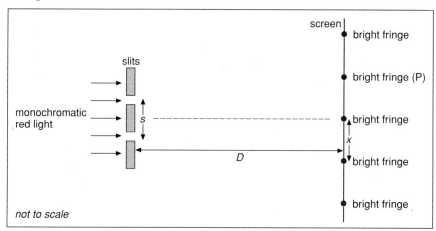

not to scale

State suitable values for *s* and *D* if clearly observable fringes are to be produced. 1]

Explain how the bright fringe labelled P is formed. [3]

What would be the effect on the fringe width *x* of

    (i)   increasing the slit separation *s*, [1]

    (ii) illuminating the slits with blue light? [1]

To obtain a superposition pattern the light from the two slits must be coherent. What is meant by the term *coherent*? [1]

15 The diagram shows a wire with a mass of 1.30 kg at one end and a vibrator at the other end.

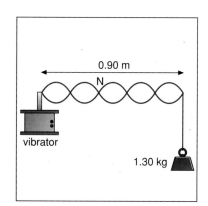

(a) How many wavelengths does the diagram show? [1]

Use your answer to calculate the wavelength λ of the stationary wave. [1]

The frequency of the vibrator is 250 Hz. Calculate the speed of the waves. [2]

(b) Point N in the diagram is a node. Copy the diagram and on it mark with an A an *antinode*. [1]

State *one* difference between a node and an antinode. [1]

Explain how a node is formed from two progressive waves. [2]

In energy terms, what is the difference between a stationary wave and a progressive wave? [2]

16 A photoelectric cell is illuminated with monochromatic light. The graph shows how the current *I* through the cell varies with the potential difference *V* across the cell.

What do you understand by the term *monochromatic*? [1]

Copy the graph, and add the following to your graph.

    (i)   A point, labelled X, to show the stopping potential.   [1]

    (ii)   A curve, labelled Y, showing what you would expect if only the wavelength of the light illuminating the cell were increased. [2]

    (iii) A curve, labelled Z, showing what you would expect if only the intensity of the original light were increased.   [2]

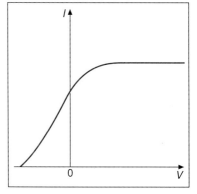

17 The graph shows how the maximum kinetic energy T of photoelectrons emitted from the surface of a metal varies with the frequency f of the incident radiation.

Why are no photoelectrons emitted at frequencies below $4.4 \times 10^{14}\,Hz$? [1]

Calculate the work function ϕ in electronvolts.   [3]

Explain how the graph supports the photoelectric equation

$$hf = T + \phi$$ [2]

How could the graph be used to find a value for the Planck constant? [1]

Copy the graph. Add a line to your graph to show the maximum kinetic energy of the photoelectrons emitted from a metal which has a greater work function.   [2]

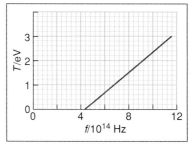

18 (a)   The following equation describes the release of electrons from a metal surface illuminated by electromagnetic radiation:

$$hf = \text{k.e.}_{max} + \phi$$

Explain briefly what you understand by each of the terms in the equation. [3]

    (b)   Calculate the momentum p of an electron travelling in a vacuum at 5% of the speed of light.   [3]

What is the de Broglie wavelength of electrons travelling at this speed? [2]

Why are electrons of this wavelength useful for studying the structure of molecules?   [2]

19 (a)   Describe briefly how you could demonstrate in a school laboratory that different elements can be identified by means of their optical spectra.   [3]

    (b)   The diagram shows a simplified energy level diagram for atomic hydrogen.

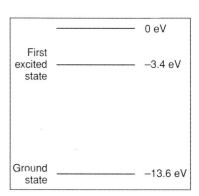

A free electron with kinetic energy 12 eV collides with an atom of hydrogen and causes it to be raised to its first excited state.

Calculate the kinetic energy of the free electron (in eV) after the collision. [1]

Calculate the wavelength of the photon emitted when the atom returns to its ground state.   [3]

Things you need to know

Chapter 1

resolution: smallest difference in a reading that an instrument can indicate

accuracy: difference between the true and the measured reading

vernier callipers: instrument used to measure distances to a resolution of 0.1 mm

micrometer screw gauge: instrument used to measure distances to a resolution of 0.01 mm

uncertainty: range around the measured reading within which the true reading lies

Chapter 2

density: mass per unit volume

rigid: something that keeps its shape

fluid: something that flows: a liquid or a gas

pressure: force acting per unit area

Chapter 3

crystal: collection of atoms having a regular structure

polycrystalline: jumbled arrangement of many crystals

amorphous: structure with no regular arrangement of its atoms

polymers: long chain molecules

Chapter 4

Hooke's law: extension is proportional to the applied force up to a certain limit

spring constant: ratio of applied force to extension produced; measure of the stiffness of the spring

stiff: requires a large tension to produce a small extension

limit of proportionality: point above which Hooke's law no longer applies

elastic limit: point where behaviour of material changes from elastic to plastic

elastic: material returns to original size and shape when applied force removed

plastic: material retains a permanent deformation when applied force is removed

Chapter 5

plastic flow: process where atoms slide over each other and produce permanent deformation

yield point: point at which plastic deformation begins

tough: material that absorbs energy by undergoing plastic deformation

brittle: material that displays no plastic deformation

Chapter 6

tensile: when stretched and put under tension

tensile stress: force applied per unit cross-sectional area

breaking stress (or **ultimate tensile stress**): largest tensile stress that the material can withstand; measure of the strength of a material

strain: extension per unit original length

Young modulus: ratio of stress to strain over linear region; gradient of initial linear part of stress–strain graph; measure of stiffness of material

Chapter 7

nucleus: tiny positive centre of an atom in which most of its mass is concentrated

nucleon: collective name for particles found in the nucleus, namely protons and neutrons

proton number (or **atomic number**) Z: number of protons in the nucleus and the number of electrons in a neutral atom

nucleon number (or **mass number**) A: total number of protons Z and neutrons N in the nucleus; indicates mass of atom

isotopes: atoms with the same number of protons but different numbers of neutrons in their nuclei

unified mass unit: one-twelfth of the mass of an atom of carbon-12 (symbol u)

relative atomic mass: mass of a nuclide in unified mass units

Chapter 8

ionises: atom given sufficient energy to release an electron and become a positive ion

alpha (α) radiation: helium nuclei emitted by some radioactive nuclei; heavily ionising (produces many ions per millimetre along its path) and short range

beta-minus (β^-) radiation: fast-moving electrons emitted by some radioactive nuclei; less ionising and consequently a larger range than alpha

beta-plus (β^+) radiation: fast-moving positrons emitted by some radioactive nuclei

gamma (γ) rays: photons of electromagnetic radiation emitted from energetic nuclei resulting from alpha or beta decay; little ionising and large range

Chapter 9

binding energy: energy released when a nucleus forms from its constituent particles; energy required to separate a nucleus into its separate particles

mass defect: difference between the mass of the nucleus and the total original mass of its constituent particles

fusion: process of joining together light nuclei to produce slightly heavier nuclei and large amounts of energy

fission: process of splitting up large nuclei into much lighter nuclei to produce large amounts of energy

Chapter 10

background radiation: emissions mainly from naturally occurring radio-isotopes; varies randomly with time

random decay: unable to predict when any given nucleus will decay, although large numbers of nuclei can be treated statistically

decay constant: probability of decay per nucleus per second

half-life: average time taken for half the nuclei of that isotope to decay

exponential decay: occurs since the rate of decay (or activity) depends on the number of undecayed nuclei present

Chapter 11

periodic motion: movement that repeats itself in a regular manner

oscillation: regular, back-and-forth motion

equilibrium position: where resultant force on oscillating body is zero

displacement x: how far, and in what direction, the body is from its equilibrium position

time trace: sketch showing variation of displacement with time

amplitude x_0: maximum displacement

cycle: a complete movement of an oscillating system

period T: time taken to cover one complete oscillation or cycle

frequency: number of complete oscillations each second

Chapter 12

simple harmonic motion (s.h.m.): oscillatory motion where the period does not depend on the amplitude

sinusoidal: shape (either sine or cosine) of the time trace associated with s.h.m.

definition of s.h.m.: motion where the acceleration (or force) is directly proportional to the displacement from a fixed point and always directed towards that point

Chapter 13

phase angle: fraction of a complete oscillation between the oscillations of one oscillator and another

in phase: in step with each other

out of phase (antiphase): completely out of step with each other

Chapter 15

natural frequency: the frequency at which a free-standing system oscillates after it has been displaced and then released

THINGS YOU NEED TO KNOW

resonance: the large-amplitude oscillations that arise as a result of an oscillatory system being driven at a frequency equal to its natural frequency

damping: forces acting against oscillatory motion, reducing amplitude

Chapter 16

electromagnetic wave: transverse combination of oscillating electric and magnetic fields

travelling wave (or progressive wave): a disturbance that transfers energy

energy flux (or intensity): energy that a wave carries perpendicularly through unit area each second

point source: emits uniformly in all directions

inverse square law: when a quantity decreases in proportion to the square of the increasing distance

Chapter 17

transverse wave: a wave where the displacements are perpendicular to the direction of propagation

longitudinal wave: a wave where the displacements are parallel to the direction of propagation

plane polarised: vibrations are confined to a single plane perpendicular to the direction of energy propagation

unpolarised: vibrations occur in a large number of planes perpendicular to the direction of energy propagation

Chapter 18

wavefront: line joining all points across adjacent rays that have exactly the same phase

wavelength: the minimum distance between two in-phase points on a wave

wave speed: the rate at which the outline of a wave travels through a medium

Chapter 19

laser: *l*ight *a*mplification by *s*timulated *e*mission of *r*adiation; an intense, and potentially dangerous, source of coherent light

diffraction: the spreading out of a wave as it passes through an aperture

ray: a narrow beam

reflection: where waves hit and rebound from a barrier and remain in the same medium

Chapter 20

refraction: the change in direction of a wave as it passes from one medium into another in which it has a different speed

Snell's law: when a ray goes from one medium to another, the ratio of the sines of the angles in the two media is a constant for the two media

Chapter 21

refractive index of a medium: ratio of speed of light in vacuum to that in the medium

monochromatic: single frequency (or wavelength)

angle of deviation: angle between original and final beam directions

dispersion: the separation of a beam into its constituent frequencies

Chapter 22

total internal reflection: 100% reflection from a boundary at which the critical angle has been exceeded

critical angle: the maximum angle of incidence at which a wave can emerge into a medium in which it moves faster

optical fibre: very thin, flexible, plastic/glass cylinder along which a beam of light can travel by total internal reflection

step-index fibre: refractive index decreases abruptly when moving from core to cladding

multimode fibre: core of diameter $50\,\mu m$ within a fibre of diameter $125\,\mu m$

monomode fibre: core of diameter 5 μm within a fibre of diameter 125 μm

Chapter 23

principle of superposition: resultant displacement at any point is equal to the vector sum of the displacements of the individual waves at that point at that instant

superposition patterns: series of positions of large- and zero-amplitude waves

constructive superposition: combination of in-phase waves to produce a wave of increased amplitude

destructive superposition: combination of out-of-phase waves to produce a wave of reduced amplitude

coherent sources: sources that maintain a constant phase relationship

Chapter 24

central maximum: line of constructive superposition along which the path difference is zero

path difference: how much further one route is than another; determines the phase of combining waves

Chapter 25

subsidiary maxima: maxima at the side of the central maximum

Chapter 26

stationary wave: a disturbance that does not transfer energy although it does have energy associated with it

node: a point on a stationary wave where the displacement is always zero

antinode: a point on a stationary wave that oscillates with the maximum amplitude

fundamental frequency: the lowest frequency at which a stationary wave occurs for a given system

harmonic frequencies: whole-number multiples of the fundamental frequency

Chapter 27

photoelectric emission: emission of electrons from a surface when illuminated with electromagnetic radiation of sufficient frequency

threshold frequency: minimum frequency that will cause photoelectric emission from a material

quantum: small packet of energy

photon: smallest amount of light you can get at a given frequency

work function: minimum amount of energy needed to release an electron from the surface of a metal

Chapter 28

stopping voltage (or **stopping potential**): voltage across a photocell that is just sufficient to stop photoelectrons reaching the receiving electrode

threshold frequency: the frequency below which no photoelectrons are emitted

electronvolt: energy transferred to an electron when it moves through a potential difference of 1 V; equivalent to 1.6×10^{-19} J

saturation: when all the emitted electrons are received by the other electrode and the maximum current flows

Chapter 29

ground state: atom with its electrons in their lowest energy positions

excited: atom with one or more electrons raised above their ground-state positions

excitation energy: energy required to raise an electron to a position above its ground state

ionisation: when an electron is completely freed from an atom, leaving behind a positive ion

ionisation energy: energy required to free an electron from the ground state of an atom

emission spectrum: range of frequencies emitted by de-exciting atoms

Chapter 31

thermionic emission: process whereby electrons are emitted from a hot filament

Equations to learn

Pressure $p = F/A$

Speed of waves $c = f\lambda$

Index

Page references in italics refer to a table or an illustration.

INDEX